TRUST
The Hand Book

Polish the gemstones of my inner crown.
Twist lovingly through the inner halls,
  the deepest passages.
My thresholds give way to the mightiest of illusions
Caress, once again, the palatial essence of my being.

Excalibur thrusts deeply into the rock
Recapturing its primeval resting place.
Ours is the kingdom and ours, the glory.
My world is full of your glory.
The earth quakes
   . . . the trumpets blast
       . . . the kingdom comes.

Behold, we reside in a land ruled by kings and princes.
You are draped in my ermine robes, our bodies exalted.
There is peace and trust and love.
I feel and know the spirit of your nobility.

Once upon a time, yields to a new surreality.
Camelot is won and ours as never before.
Fairy tales and evil queens are banished forever.

TRUST

The Hand Book

A Guide to the
Sensual and Spiritual
Art of Handballing

Bert Herrman

Alamo Square Press
San Francisco

Sections of this book have been adapted from articles in *TRUST/The Hand-balling Newsletter* © 1988-1991 by Alamo Square Press.

Library of Congress Catalog Card Number: 91-076792

ISBN: 0-9624751-5-7

TO OUR FALLEN BROTHERS
who shared with us their souls
and who live on in our memories.

Acknowledgements

I owe thanks to many who made this book possible:

To the late Peter Larkin: your book, *The Divine Androgyne According to Purusha*, opened my mind to a new generation of thinking. Your legacy of the remaining copies of the book went a long way to enable Alamo Square Press to get started.

To Jerry B., Richard K., Greg O., and Eric S.: your magical vision provided me with the essential information to bridge the gap from book learning to hands-on and hands-in knowledge.

To William J. Kapla, M.D.: for generously taking the time to go over this book to make sure that it was medically accurate. Your suggestions made this book considerably more valuable.

To the readers of *TRUST/The Handballing Newsletter:* you have been my family for the last three and a half years. Ours is a community of very special people, people willing to step beyond the conventional to reach for the universal. I have a special love and closeness for you all.

Table of Contents

PART TWO
THE SPIRITUALITY OF HANDBALL

Introduction

Since the Fourth Century when St. Augustine gave up his profligate life and ruthlessly deserted his mistresses to follow the way of the Church, Christianity and Western civilization have damned the pleasures of the flesh. The Roman Church discovered that it best controlled the people when it controlled their genitalia. The Protestant churches and other religious bodies have adopted this useful device to keep the people in line.

But earlier cultures knew the ability of sexual pleasure to lift humankind beyond the mundane. The *Kama Sutra* of Hinduism went into great length on techniques of lovemaking. Although written records from earlier religions are scarce, their pottery and carvings show the interweaving of religion and sexuality.

In the magnificent Angkor Watt of Cambodia, on pottery from the early civilizations of South America and Rome, in fact in every school of "erotic" pottery known, there is record of men and women penetrating each other with their hands as well as their genitals. We easily forget that the erotic, *naughty* status of this pottery reflects the value judgments of later cultures. Esoteric sexual practice was an integral part of pre-Christian Europe and the Far East, often both heterosexual and homosexual.

Certainly, wherever there was a man or woman and an imagination, there was a person pleasuring himself or herself with whatever device fit the available orifices.

In Tantric Yoga, schools of spiritual study that traveled north and east from India, the energies of the body, including sexual energies, were harnessed to bring men and women in touch with the Divine. Few of their techniques are recorded or available. It is said that "Those who know do not speak, and those who speak do not know." But seekers have come back with knowledge from a sufficient number of dependable sources to reliably say that insertion of the hand into the anus in a ritual and sacred context has long been a part of advanced Tantric Yoga.

Visitors from monasteries in both Christian and Eastern religions have reported monastics well-versed in this art.

While public record in modern culture of the activity of handballing (fisting, FF)* can be traced back no further than the gay sexual revolution of the late 1960s and 1970s, older gay men report that this activity was spoken about decades earlier. The activity has probably been practiced by individuals in private since the beginning of recorded time.

---

* This book will exclusively use the term "handballing" because the two more prevalent terms "fisting and "fist-fucking" are often interpreted as representing an act that is crude and violent. Moreover, seldom is the hand actually used as a clenched fist.

It wasn't until the current century that world over-population and effective contraception made sexual exploration for pleasure at best somewhat publicly acceptable. Gay men, less dominated by the pairing syndrome of women and straights, began experimenting with handballing in small private clubs in the the late 1960s. In San Francisco, Los Angeles and New York, small groups formed to venture into group experiences of sharing physical ecstasy through this activity.

In San Francisco, the term FFA officially stood for "Final Faith of America." In the East it was euphemised as the "Fall Festival Association." By the heyday of gay liberation in the late 1970s, handballing was a standard part of the gay male sexual repertoire, especially in San Francisco, Los Angeles and New York. A joke popular on the East Coast went: "What's the difference between a San Francisco gay and a bowling ball?" The answer: "You can only get three fingers into a bowling ball."

By 1980, there were private handballing clubs in San Francisco, Los Angeles, Denver, Chicago, New York, Philadelphia, Washington and Miami. There were commercial clubs or bathhouses that encouraged this practice in many more cities.

The 1970s were no doubt a period of wretched excess. Gay men, heavily oppressed by the greater culture, had a hard time distinguishing between acting out their freedom and acting out the degradation in which they were held by the dominant straight culture. Many allowed themselves to get swallowed up by drugs and approached their lovemaking as "pig" or animal sex.

At the same time, the gay leather culture was developing. Gay men took on the attire of motorcycle riders, cowboys, construction workers and other macho icons of the greater culture. It was a chance to put aside the effeminate images of the past and construct new images of personal power. Experimental sex was a key to the leather culture: bondage, flagellation, body piercing, fantasy, handballing and a myriad of other activities. These were often correctly or incorrectly lumped together as S&M (sado-masochism). The dominant sexual activity of the period, however, remained penile-anal sex.

In 1981, Peter Allison Larkin published a book called *The Divine Androgyne According to Purusha.** Larkin, a former Benedictine monastic with a broad background in spiritual thought and psychology, developed a theory that gay men through handballing and other esoteric sexual practices could produce an advanced spiritual state in line with the concepts of Tantric Yoga.

Larkin (Purusha) hoped to form a collective of 13 men to develop his theories in his "Sanctuary," a monastic retreat he constructed in the desert outside of San Diego. But his Sanctuary never got its proper trial.

In the early 1980s, AIDS struck the gay community with a vengeance. Handballers, weakened by heavy drug abuse, unprotected sex and a history of combining handball with traditional anal sex (a lethal combination), died in inordinate numbers. With the details of virus transmission still

---

* Larkin, Peter Allison, *The Divine Androgyne According to Purusha* (San Diego: Sanctuary Publications, 1981).

little understood, handballing was placed on the top of the "un-safe sex" list. There it stood until 1988, when medical science was able to pinpoint the spread of HIV infection to transmission of body fluids.

At this time, health agencies in areas that kept up with scientific development began to downgrade protected handballing to "low-risk" behavior. It is hard to dispute the fact that handballers using latex gloves are in no greater risk of infection than hospital workers, protected by the same gloves.

In 1988, ads for *TRUST/The Handballing Newsletter* first appeared in gay publications across the country. For the past four years, *TRUST* has been spreading information on how to keep handballing safer and healthier. *TRUST* has fostered a philosophy of approaching sex as a celebration of life rather than a means of self-degradation. At the end of 1991, *TRUST* has over 1000 subscribers around the world and regularly shares information on the activities of the four remaining handball clubs. Subscribers are both men and women.

The time has now come to reach a broader audience with the many discoveries we have made; to bring to other men and women, both straight and gay, the possibilities of sensual and spiritual experience far beyond the ordinary. It is in this vein that this book is offered.

Bert Herrman, 1991

PART ONE

THE SENSUALITY OF HANDBALL

Chapter 1. What is Handballing?

Handballing is manipulation of the anal canal, the rectum and perhaps the descending and transverse colon with the hand, and sometimes the forearm and beyond, in such a manner as to be sensually pleasurable. While it may sound uncomfortable and unpleasant to the uninitiated, so does all sexual activity. The joy comes from the feeling, not the anatomical description.

The Ecstasy

With handballing, pleasurable sensations of other anal intercourse (such as manipulation of the prostate in a man) are at play, but there is also an intense intimacy created by the very nature of the significant connectedness. Participants often describe venturing into other levels of consciousness or even blasting into outer space. The receiver often reaches intense orgasm and the top feels corresponding pleasure (often reaching orgasm, as well) from the connectedness of the experience.

Handballing is often called the closest thing to giving birth to a child. There is a feeling of being open and full of your companion. Participants speak of an ecstasy beyond the limits of rational understanding. Often the ecstasy seems new and unbelievable each time, because the extent of the feeling is so immense that the memory can not grasp its magnitude. There is a feeling of trust between the partners, impossible to reach by any other means. Both giver and receiver speak of having direct connection with their partner's *soul*.

In contemporary history, handballing has been mainly the interest of a small dedicated coterie of gay men, but in recent years adventurous lesbians and heterosexuals have begun venturing into this new territory. While women do not have a prostate gland, the many other feelings are open to them plus, if they wish, the simultaneous massage of the vaginal cavity, bringing in an entirely different combination of sensations.

It is important to note that while such sensation may be sport for some people, for many of us it is lovemaking in the most unequivocal fashion. Often handballing is first ventured into by two dedicated partners seeking greater ways of physically expressing their love and connectedness.

Among gay men, handballing may be a means of group connection with three, four or more participants. This may be a a sensual orgy or a ritual of group love and affection depending on the mindsets of the participants. Both situations are common; sometimes the two are hard to distinguish.

The Risk of Harm

The initial reaction of most people and the lingering doubt of almost everyone is: "Isn't this dangerous?" It is and it isn't. The greatest risk is trauma: bruising and soreness to the muscles, and possibly scratching or puncturing the lining of the digestive tract. If the participants do not know or care what they are doing, these problems are not only possible, they are likely.

Driving a car or even crossing a busy street is also dangerous, if one does not learn what one is doing and take the necessary precautions. In life we learn to take certain risks to derive benefits. Skilled handballers know they are less likely to put their lives in danger making love, than they are driving home afterwards.

An inexperienced receiver (bottom), owes it to him or herself to learn at the hands of someone who has significant experience or has accumulated the necessary knowledge to do it safely and harmlessly. You also want to be with people who care about you and what they are doing. This is no place to deal with people on power trips.

An experienced bottom knows how to select partners who can be trusted. Without such discretion, a bottom will not likely have a long history of handballing.

Tops usually learn their skills with experienced bottoms, or in many cases, people develop both skills together. There is much to be said for the joys of versatility. The best tops are usually skilled at bottom as well. This frequent lack of role-playing makes handballing unusual in the domain of sexuality.

Much of the succeeding material in this book will give
the essential points of technique that will make the experience
of both giving and receiving easier, healthier and more satisfying. We will also go into greater depth on avoiding other
health risks.

Infection

In recent years, the major concern of infection is the
HIV (AIDS) virus, but sexual activity, especially activity in-
volving the rectal area, may also expose a person to the risk
of infection from parasites, hepatitis and the traditional
sexually-transmitted diseases.

Proper cleansing of the digestive tract, effective use of
latex gloves, careful control of lubricants and general clean-
liness (all of which will be discussed at length in successive
chapters) can virtually eliminate the risks of infection.

It is also important that people pay attention to any
sexual emissions to be sure they do not come into contact
with their partner's mucous membranes. Bottoms should
refrain from other receptive anal sex for at least several days
after handballing, in order to give their interiors a chance to
fully mend, so as to avoid infection from other means.

Addiction

While it is recommended that handballers refrain from
using heavy drugs, many do not. Drugs can enhance the sen-
suality of the experience and can make receiving easier, but
the damage done to body and mind by the drugs themselves

heavily outweighs such enhancement.

The most serious drug commonly used is crystal meth-amphetamines (crystal, speed, crank). More will be said about this in Chapter 6. Crystal is highly addictive. Cocaine is also commonly used, especially in areas (Florida and Texas) where it is relatively inexpensive. Both drugs are most dangerous and addictive when taken intravenously, but when either are used on a regular basis (weekly or bi-weekly) by any means, users learn to unconsciously associate drugs and sex. Often they cannot give up the drugs without giving up sex as well.

Chapter 2. Paraphernalia

Years of experience with handballing have led to a significant arsenal of materials to keep play safe and comfortable. Here are some important suggestions:

Gloves

Medical people agree: latex gloves drastically reduce the health risks of handballing. Regardless of the HIV status of you and/or your partner, don't leave home (or stay home) without them.

The inside of one's body provides ideal transfer conditions for all sorts of microorganisms including the HIV virus. Surface abrasions in the walls of the large intestines (colon) are an ordinary occurrence even in normal conditions. No matter how clean one gets, one's insides will not be sterile, and the body secretes mucous in the colon in the natural course.

The major threat of infection is for the top. Minor

paper cuts, scratches and sores on your hands cannot be avoided. Microorganisms can even enter the system at the base of the fingernails. Only gloves can help you avoid this threat. For the bottom, gloves minimize the possibility of scratches from the fingernails and soreness from rough and calloused hands.

Health professionals I have spoken to agree that standard disposable examination gloves are usually sufficient even on depth explorations. Longer, "opera length" or calving gloves are not necessary unless the top has cuts or scratches above the glove line. These can usually be easily spotted.

Long gloves are usually heavier and therefore less sensitive to feeling. They are usually reusable. However, it is difficult for the top to remain conscious of how lubricated these long gloves are at various points, and therefore it is more likely that at some point they will become dry and uncomfortable for the bottom.

Latex Not Vinyl

For many years, only vinyl (rather than latex) gloves were available in drugstores. Vinyl gloves are better than nothing, but they feel scratchy and rough and permit less sensitivity. They break down with standard wear from lubricants. It is not uncommon to hear people say, "I can't take it with gloves." Usually you find the gloves they have been using are vinyl. Do everything you can to find latex gloves. Remember also to always use plenty of lubricant on the gloves so they don't get hot from the friction.

Many brands of latex examination gloves are currently on the market. Most are imported from the Orient. Health, mortuary and law enforcement personnel are now wearing these gloves. You can usually find them in drugstores, but in some areas you must go to a medical supply house. The gloves are now being used for many purposes, so don't be shy.

Non-sterile examination gloves that fit either hand are normally available in small, medium and large, but some suppliers handle extra-large. Sterile gloves are available in half sizes. These come in pairs designated left and right. However, the area is not sterile to begin with so sterile gloves offer no advantage.

Gloves that fit too tight can split while you're using them; gloves that are too large will wrinkle and irritate. Most brands of gloves have rolled cuffs and are coated with talcum powder or corn starch. Cut the cuffs off and rinse off the powder before use to avoid these additional causes of irritation.

News is now coming in that latex gloves, like latex condoms, are subject to deterioration through exposure to air. This means you should try to keep your gloves in the box until you need them; the gloves you've kept in your back pocket for two months—like the condom in your wallet—may not offer the best protection because of microscopic holes that increase in size when the glove stretches over your hand. Never reuse gloves or insert them into more than one person.

Additional Infection

A foolish line heard occasionally is, "I'm already HIV-positive; why should I bother with gloves?" The reasons are clear. First, there are apparently various mutant strains of HIV virus; exposure to multiple strains will increase the threat to your system. Also, if you are one who is immuno-compromised, it is all the more important that you not expose yourself to other disease-causing organisms; the list of those that can be spread through direct contact would astound you (see Chapter 7).

If you are so naive as to take your partner's word on faith that he or she is HIV-negative, you should have your head examined along with your blood. Even if you are both HIV-negative, you will be subjecting yourself to other organisms that can jeopardize your general health and perhaps, in time, your immune system. Don't even think of taking a chance; both top and bottom are in danger.

Other Cautions

Tops should be careful about fluid emissions. Such fluids should not be allowed in direct contact with the partner or their own gloved hand. Tops should change gloves often and used gloves should be disposed of immediately.

It is true that latex will breakdown in time with exposure to oils (vegetable or mineral). We suggest that if play is to be very extended that the top change gloves from time to time. However, since drugs are usually necessary to permit that sort of extended play, such clear judgment is unlikely.

25

Lubricants

The question of the ideal lubricant for handballing remains unanswered. The great majority use vegetable shortening, the standard being Crisco® from Procter & Gamble (regular not butter-flavored). There are a few diehards who use the mineral oil-based lubes commercially developed for sexual purposes. The only advantage of these products is that they do not impart an odor. In the volume necessary for handball they are very expensive.

It is true that vegetable shortening has been reported to break down the latex in condoms in laboratory tests so that the HIV virus could pass through. The same goes for mineral oil-based preparations. However, latex gloves are heavier than condoms and except on very extended play, there is little reason to expect glove breakdown.

The problem is that water-based lubricants (containing neither vegetable or mineral oil) rarely provide the lubrication necessary for handball. The possible trauma (ouch) from not using enough grease to do the job is far more dangerous than the remote possibility of glove breakdown.

Some people produce a considerable amount of mucous in their intestines when sexually aroused. These people have an easier time with water-based lubricants and keeping their insides greased up is no trouble at all.

Whatever your choice, it is important that containers of lubricant never be used for the interior of more than one person, since this is a likely way to spread unfriendly microorganisms.

Cans of vegetable shortening are sterile until opened.

26

So individual portions for each bottom should be set aside from the main supply. But don't keep the portions around too long; bacteria from your skin will grow in them. Refrigeration slows this process, but each warming will start things growing again. Clean containers frequently—your health is worth the cost.

Bottoms should each have their own container and these tubs should be cleaned out or trashed at the end of the evening. Plastic 8 oz. margarine bowls hold the perfect amount for anything but the longest sessions and the hungriest bottoms. All greasy items should be disinfected as soon as possible, and all due care should be taken not to expose yourself to used grease. After play, both top and bottom should scrub exposed body parts with antibacterial soap or scrub.

We also suggest that tops (especially those who are HIV-negative) should rub a nonoxynol-9 preparation (spermicidal gel) on their hand before inserting into a glove, in the event of leakage. While these formulations effectively kill the HIV virus, tests have shown that they are also very irritating to the kind of cells that line the rectum and vagina. This means that nonoxynol-9 may allow the virus to more effectively penetrate faster. So limit this stuff to *inside* the glove.

Most importantly, never think that a condom is going to do you any good after you have taken a hand with an oil-based lubricant. Always wait at least a day or two before taking anything else inside.

Covers

Time was when sheets and towels were what we used to cover regular bedding or whatever was on top of the selected play area. Laundry time was not much fun.

Today, most handballers have discovered underpads or "chucks" as they are called in hospitals. These pads are blue plastic on one side and absorbant on the other. They are used in hospitals and sick beds for incontinence. They are inexpensive, sold at most drug stores and easily discarded.

Some people use special rubberized play sheets created for this purpose. Vinyl mattress covers get dry and uncomfortable from contact with shortening. Keep a play sheet under the underpad for accidents. This should be washed and disinfected frequently.

Rolls of paper towels nearby are a must. It is wise to cut off three or four double lengths before each session of play and have them within grabbing distance after the session is over. At that point no one is any shape to neatly tear towels off a roll. You can further facilitate cleanup by having a double layer over the underpad to pick up lubricant fallout.

If you do get shortening on towels and sheets, there are proven methods for dealing with the situation. But do it quickly and don't expect 100 percent results.

For heavily soiled loads you can start by soaking the linens in Spic'N Span® household cleaner and Pine Sol® disinfectant (a half cup of each) in the bathtub in very hot water to get the big clumps to dissolve. Rinse in clear hot water. Then squeeze them out and wash in the washing machine with laundry soap and a half cup each of Spic 'N

Span® and Pine Sol®. Avoid detergents which will set the odor.

Next, put them through the washer again with a half to a full cup of white vinegar. The vinegar will even help cut the shortening residue from past washings. Depending on what else is on the linens, you may want to run them through one more time with bleach.

Slings

While some people prefer beds for lovemaking, others prefer a carpet, a covered floor or maybe a secluded lawn on a warm evening. Still others swear by the sling. This is a specially fabricated affair crafted usually of leather, plastic webbing or canvas. It is normally suspended from the ceiling or from high on walls with metal chains. You can also suspend it from strong bedposts or a frame especially created for this purpose. If you suspend one from walls or ceilings, make sure that the hooks to hold the chains are screwed into beams or studs with the ability to bear the weight.

Slings are usually suspended by four chains. The idea is to allow the bottom to lie comfortably inside with head higher than the waist. Usually a pillow goes under the head. The bottom's legs either wrap around the two lower chains, or the chains support fleece-lined cuffs that securely hold the ankles.

The sling brings the bottom's posterior about waist high on the standing top, though the top may prefer to sit on a chair or stool.

While this device may sound esthetically threatening to

the romantic (and it does limit kissing and other romantic business), it is highly practical and allows the top the maximum degree of flexibility. It also gives the bottom the ability to swing with or against the motion of the top.

Slings for this purpose can be purchased from stores that sell sexually-oriented leather goods. A talented person knowledgeable in what they like in a sling can craft their own.

Shower Divertor System

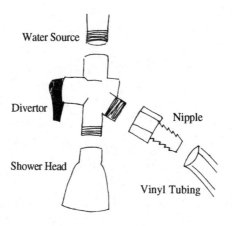

Parts for a shower divertor system can be purchased for under $20 at most hardware stores. Divertor piece may be in a different configuration. It will wear best if metal rather than plastic.

Chapter 3. Preparation

Before getting into things, handballing requires appropriate preparation. For the bottom this often begins the evening before, preparing for the necessary enema.

The Pre-handball Diet

While proper diet is important for everyone, it is even more important for handballers.

One of the major problems with enemas is that they tend to kill off friendly bacteria and microflora that aid digestion, produce vitamins and keep us well. These bacteria can be largely replaced by adding acidophilus milk (available everywhere and undistinguishable in taste from ordinary milk) and yogurt with active cultures to your diet. For those who avoid dairy, acidophilus powder is available. You can also help protect the helpful bacteria by cutting down or eliminating coffee, which unmercifully attacks these friendly little buggers.

Before Cleaning

What to eat before cleaning out varies greatly from person to person, depending in part on how deeply you cleanse and the nature of your regular diet. A person on a healthy diet will normally process their food within 18 to 36 hours after eating. It will take longer if one regularly consumes large quantities of red meat and fat. Of course, what you wish to accomplish is to have everything that is coming through come out when you clean, and have the rest stay in place so that you can play in confidence but not be haunted by undue hunger.

The theory then is to eat things that will pass through quickly, 19 to 36 hours before cleaning. Fruits, vegetables and whole grains are best. Red meat and fatty foods are to be avoided. One person I know eats nothing but cantaloupes the day before. Some people take Metamucil® (or a generic brand of natural vegetable laxative) the night before, to gently clear out bulk from the system. Do not take anything harsh that could irritate your intestinal lining. During the entire period, avoid eating nuts as well as poppy, sesame and other seeds that can filter through at uneven speed and foul up the whole process.

For the final 18 hours eat very little. What you do eat should be food that will digest slowly and with little residue. Dairy foods and eggs are great (a good time for your yogurt). A slice of plain pizza might hit the spot or some fish or chicken. Take vitamins, as necessary, to keep your strength and nutrition up. A quarter hour before you begin washing, consider a hot drink to hurry anything through that's going through. Coffee is most effective but hard on your system in general. Chamomile tea is an excellent relaxant. Try not to eat anything after cleaning out, since eating will renew peristalsis, the body's system for passing everything through, all the way down the line.

During play, apple juice or even an apple is a good idea because of their highly soothing qualities. Try mixing it with some cold herb tea. However, any cold drink will do. Keep something ready; your mouth will get dry.

The Enema*

Properly cleaning out before receiving in handball is absolutely essential. Fecal matter left in the system can cause abrasions to the abdominal lining, besides spreading disease and being altogether unpleasant. However, douching is never a totally foolproof system. The body often has thoughts of its own. If things are not totally clean, it is best for both partners to take it in stride, stop action and perhaps give the bottom another chance to clean out. While you may be looking for honey in the beehive, occasionally you are going to find bees! For everbody's sake don't overreact!

There are three major types of equipment you can use to clean out: the shower divertor set-up, the bulb syringe and the ordinary fountain syringe (often a combination enema bag/hot water bottle).

---

* Thanks to Frank E. Ball, coordinator of the Fraternity of Enema Buddies for information used in this section.

Shower Divertor Method

The most popular device is the now-ubiquitous aluminum nozzle attachment (sometimes referred to as "the silver bullet" or shower bidet) that is rigged up to the shower. This is simple, a single purchase, and does the job. It gives you immediate control of the temperature and flow of the water and is always hanging there when you need it. These are available in sex shops and through mail order.

A less costly version can be put together with a standard shower divertor piece, a metal nipple and a length of vinyl tubing—all available at most hardware stores (see illustration page 30). This set-up may have to be replaced more often, and you'll have to take a blade and round the exposed edges of the tubing so it doesn't scratch. The tubing does allow you to plan extra length for a wider selection of positions and can, if you wish, be drawn inside more deeply. However, we suggest a special enema hosetip if you are planning colonic depths.

If you wish to add to the esthetics of the process, you can get a long enough piece of hose to stretch to the toilet. Leave the far end of the hose in the bowl when you initiate the flow. Do carefully figure out all your logistics beforehand so you don't saturate the entire bathroom.

Do be careful—direct plumbing hook-ups allow the risk of unexpected changes in temperature, volume and pressure. These can be uncomfortable or even dangerous.

Set the temperature to your liking (someplace between lukewarm and body temperature). Set the flow to a slow-to-moderate rate. Slide the tip inside and take as much water as you can, hold it a few seconds, or as long as possible, then let it out (usually right into the tub, where you can squirt it all down the drain). If in the tub or shower, you can assume whatever position works for you: standing, squatting, lying on your back or even on your hands and knees. Repeat again and again (usually three or four times) until you are taking a large amount comfortably and running clean. You may find yourself leaving the bathroom for periods of time, while the water wends its way back down. If water gets captured in higher sections of your digestive system, you can press on your system, dance around a little or lie on your left side to aid gravity (see the illustration of the digestive tract on page 42).

The Bulb Syringe

The bulb syringe is most easily used in a bathtub filled with water. The most comfortable way is to lie on your back, fill the syringe with water and draw the tip inside. Then squeeze the bulb, which will inject the water at the pace you want. Keeping the bulb squeezed with your hand, withdraw it and, keeping it totally submerged, permit it to refill automatically.

Simply repeat the insertion, squeezing and refilling until you feel comfortably full of water. In order to let out this enema, however, it will be necessary for you to get up, step out of the tub and go to the toilet. Afterwards, you can get back into the tub and repeat the process until you are clean.

The Fountain Syringe

The regular fountain syringe is hung overhead to let gravity do the work of filling you with an adequate amount of water. It can be used in the tub or shower or on the toilet. The standard fountain syringe holds two quarts of water; most people experienced in handballing can hold that amount quite easily. In fact, as you get used to the sensation of taking larger and larger enemas, it should not be long before you can hold three or four quarts. You may want to keep an extra pitcher handy to refill the bag (open type) so that you can learn to hold this amount.

Another way to get a sufficient reservoir of water is to attach two regular bags with a "T" connector, or better yet, obtain a large gallon-plus, heavy duty "Sherema" enema bag, which is a favorite among those who want the most sophisticated equipment.

You can use any position that is comfortable for you with the fountain syringe, including lying on the left side with the right leg drawn up over the left leg (the common hospital position). A hook on the ceiling over your bathtub or shower is a good place to hang your bag and it also facilitates watering hanging house plants.

The fountain syringe is the mostly highly recommended method of cleaning out. It gives you the best gauge of how much water you're taking and also allows you to include additives. For instance, you might try some baking soda in your next-to-the-last enema water. This has a soothing effect on the colon in addition to giving you just enough stimulation to evacuate completely.

Here are a few additional enema tips:

• Try to allow yourself at least two full hours between the end of your final enema and the beginning of your handball activities. This will give your colon the opportunity to reabsorb traces of water that may remain after your final rinse.

• Don't be too eager to experiment with Fleets® enemas or other chemical enema preparations. These are often quite harsh on the gut and may cause your intestines to become too irritated for intense handball activity.

• A little wine added to your douche can give you a pleasant high, but is irritating to the intestinal lining. The wine will be quickly released into the blood stream and can cause a stronger effect than you expected. This maneuver is not recommended.

• Mucous discharge after your final rinse is a good sign. This is the body's way of restoring natural protection to the inner surface of your intestines.

• You may find a final rinse of somewhat cooler water soothing to your system.

• Remember to clean your hose tip if you share. Liquid bleach will do the job well. An antimicrobial scrub is also fine, if you're concerned about spilling the bleach or burning yourself because you didn't rinse it all off.

• Your choice of enema technique may have to take into consideration the ability of your tub or shower to drain particulate matter. Drain back-ups are no fun. If in doubt, keep a bathroom plunger on hand.

Some handballing partners include "cleaning out" as an

initial and integral part of their regular foreplay, enjoying the mental and physical stimulation of giving and receiving, an erotic build-up through progressively larger enemas until they are thoroughly cleaned out and ready for more solid pleasure. In addition to taking the time together to get ready, you also have the opportunity to experience unusual intimacy and sensuousness with your partner before the actual handball scene commences.

Other Preparation

There are a number of things that can and should be done before starting. Some people use this time to enjoy substances to help them relax or get into the mood. While such substances are not recommended, a list of some of those commonly used is included in Chapter 6 along with their attested advantages and risks.

Shaving

Everyone has some hair growing on the inner sides of the butt. If this hair is long it may get pulled when a hand is inserted. If this is any problem, and it seldom is, shaving or trimming your butt may be the answer. If you're dexterous you can do it yourself. Or maybe it will be a turn-on for your partner. Be careful to avoid nicks. You may have to do it again within a few weeks and the stubble will itch a bit as it grows out. Use a soothing lotion afterwards.

The Top

Before beginning to play, the top should check hands and arms. If there are any major cuts or open sores on the lower arms, the top should consider another activity for the evening or find calving gloves that will cover the exposed area. Minor cuts may be covered with NewSkin® liquid bandage, but should still be covered by a latex glove, if possible.

Fingernails should be cut as short as possible. Rough edges should be filed down; calluses on the hands should be softened as much as possible.

The Space

Now is the time to get your play area together. Make sure that surfaces are disinfected and scrubbed clean of any traces of past play. Underpads, paper towels and lubricant should be available. Drinks should be cold. You should also ready whatever else will make the encounter more pleasant. Candles or indirect light will be easier on the eyes. Incense is a nice touch.

New Age music is most universally appreciated. Most people find that listening to the music keeps both partners in synch. New Age music tends to be constantly changing and encourages creativity in the top. Rock music with a strong, repetitive beat will tend to make the action repetitive and violent, making the bottom sore.

It is always good when partners can discuss their ideas of play beforehand, so they can establish a mood that will satisfy both. If the top has set up the dungeon and is blaring Wagner when the bottom is expecting to cuddle to Montovani, you may be in trouble!

If one chooses to use some sort of toys to loosen the bottom before the main event, they should be cleaned and ready to use. Dildoes that are not soft and pliable or that have any wire inside should never be used; they should always have a base or handle to facilitate extraction and should not be inserted in more than one person without thorough disinfection. Incorrect use of dildoes is far more dangerous than handball.

Building Rapport

In order to reach the necessary rapport, it is best to take some time getting to know each other before you begin. A top should try to discover the fantasies of the bottom and keep them in mind so the two partners can create a consciousness together. If the bottom has no particular ideas to begin with perhaps the top will have some, keeping close watch that the effects are positive.

Whatever the fantasy, it is imperative that bottoms feel secure that their welfare is being respected. If both parties are not well-experienced it is reassuring for the top to verbalize commitment to the fact that "stop" means that the top will stop in place and that "out" means the top will slowly and carefully come out. A smart bottom will likely test early on that tops intend to be true to their word.

If either or both of you are adept at body rubs or massage, this is a great idea before you get into the heavy play.

Not only does it give the two of you more chance for caring body contact, but it also relaxes mind and muscles, assuring easier entrance.

Foreplay

What gets two people excited is very much between them. Kissing and cuddling is important to some people while flagellation will turn on others. Many gay men have discovered that nipples are as much erogenous zones for them as breasts are for women. Properly exerted pressure on the nipples at just the cutting edge of pain can stimulate the body's endorphines, emitting internal secretions into the system that counter with euphoria what might otherwise be registered by the body as unpleasant.

When the time is right, the top or aggressive bottom sets an underpad under the derrière in question (whether on the bed, the floor or the sling). All necessary items being within reach, the top puts on the glove or gloves (removing the cuff and rinsing off the powder if not done in advance), fondles the body parts that elicit the correct reaction and you're ready to begin.

The Lower Digestive System

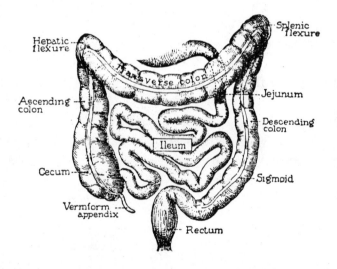

Chapter 4. Technique for Tops

There is a slender border between pain and pleasure. This is the path of ecstasy, the route a hand should take on the way to the depths of another's soul. Remaining on that path requires concentration from both parties.

Contrary to the beliefs of the uninitiated, handball is nothing at all like stuffing a turkey. Most of us will attest to the fact that handballing is likely the most intense intimacy that two human beings will ever share.

For some people, topping is a power trip where they can express control over another human being. Such people should be given punching bags and kept far from us. A knowledgeable handballing top understands that such control is illusionary.

A captain steering a ship through a turbulent ocean knows that it is the water that is in control; the captain's job is tuning in and maneuvering through the tides and currents. So it is with handballing.

When you are buried inside another person, it is their

body you must tune in with. When bottoms permit you this privilege, they are putting trust in you, a trust that you will respect their vulnerability and a trust that you will synchronize with the flow of their body to create a combined energy that neither one of you could ever create on your own.

A good top is totally focused on the needs of the bottom. It is as if there are not two, but one, person present and you have become part of each other. When you are focused in this manner, the physical ecstasy of the bottom is immediately intuited by the top. The joy is shared.

Remember that each person is built differently and there is no one best way to do anything. Whoever thinks so will fail miserably somewhere along the line. Be flexible. Be conscious of the uniqueness of your partner. Almost every suggestion of technique offered here will not work well with somebody.

Getting Started

The initial entry is most important for setting the pace of the evening. No matter what the illusion, a top should never push in, but should be gently sucked in by the bottom. The top should lightly massage the walls of the orifice, seeking a motion that seems to flow with the body of the bottom. It's often best to give some gentle resistance to the bottom's pulling—to let the bottom know that if they're going to take it, they're going to have to work for it. With an inexperienced or timid bottom, it is often the consistency and gentleness of this resistance that will establish just how deep an intimacy will be established.

If the bottom registers pain or feels about to feel pain, slow down and back off slightly and relieve the pressure. If the sides of the opening get warm, they are filling with blood and the bottom is frightened and tightening up. Slow down until the heat subsides and the bottom encourages you onward.

Establishing the Flow

A person's butt is as unique as fingerprints. The chemistry between two partners will also be unique. It is much like music: the bottom provides the tempo, the top responds with the melody, the bottom reacts with the harmony. When things are working, it all just flows.

While there are good tops who have never bottomed, they are always better after both experiences. It is nearly impossible to conceptualize the effects and nuances that just a minor movement will have on the body of the bottom. Bottoms, too, will have more respect for the efforts of their tops if they sincerely work at learning both arts.

Handballing is a constantly creative process. Like a jazz jam session, each party takes some initiative in leading the music through intricate and fanciful maneuvers. While the top and/or bottom may have some general agenda in mind (slow depth, gentle stretching or an "in and out" motion that might simulate the movements of more familiar objects of entry) both parties are best off to tune in with each other and allow the music to simply happen.

45

Warming Up

After the desired foreplay, the top works a gloved hand down to the partner's bottom and strokes it gently with a finger before entry.

Assume the position that works best for both of you, physically and mentally. Some partners like the bottom resting on the back with legs in the air, legs on the top's shoulders or somehow constrained. This position allows your eyes to meet and you can occasionally break into titplay or other lovemaking as the process continues.

Many bottoms prefer a sling, when available. Others like to be belly down and butt up, on all fours (doggie style). Some bottoms will request that you try doggie style later on, since this position provides the least bending of the rectum and often permits easier depth. Rarely will a bottom want it while flat on the abdomen, since this puts the rectum at a difficult angle.

Initial Entry

Before you begin, cover your entire glove with lubricant and cover your partner's opening with a generous coating.

To begin the lovemaking, slowly press in and out with one finger. When there is no resistance, increase to two fingers. Try just the thumb, using the broad base of the thumb to broaden the opening even further, twisting slowly. When the bottom is ready, work in three fingers and onward till you find yourself to the knuckles. Each time you come out grab more lubricant. Make sure there is plenty of it ahead of you. Drying out can be a major cause of discomfort for both of you.

Some tops put gloves on both hands, offering themselves the use of all ten fingers and that many more ways to be creative until the bottom has been worked up to the whole hand.

In most people, initial opening is a slow process. Never rush. This should be enjoyed by both partners as an integral part of the evening's pleasure. It is at this point that you begin feeling each other out mentally and tuning in to each other's needs.

Always start entry of the full hand in the position of a swan's head; fingers may slowly wiggle to aid in admission, gently messaging the sides of the passage. You can broaden the beak of the bird as the bottom relaxes and gives way to your entry.

Slowly broadening your fingers when you are at rest or pulling back and narrowing them as you proceed inward, will often tease the butt and have it begging for more.

In the initial entry, some people prefer a slow, gentle but firm pressure, constantly inwards. These people will react by greeting you, pulling you in as you maintain the pressure. Others may prefer to do all the pulling from the inside, demanding that you provide a slight backward resistance. Still other bottoms will react best if you press slowly in and out, simulating the entrance into the body of something with which they are more familiar. Some people will enjoy different techniques at different times. The more often the two of you are together, the better you will know the bottom's preferences.

Do not make any sudden moves or jerks; this will cause the bottom to tighten up. You want your technique to be slow, smooth and graceful. You want the bottom to be paying attention to the pleasure, not to your technique.

Slipping In

You will often find that the largest challenge for even experienced bottoms is the entrance to the initial cavity (the rectum). Do not assume (unless you have been with the person before and know otherwise) that this will be quick and easy. Some bottoms react best to a slow twisting in. Others (especially those with extensive dildo experience) will want you to go straight in with minimum twisting. Listen to what your bottom is saying with words and body. If in doubt, ask.

Always make sure there is plenty of lubricant in front of you, on your hand and on your wrist. When in doubt, use more lubricant. (But remember, never pull out or go in too fast, even to regrease; your tiniest change in speed and pressure will feel greatly exaggerated to the bottom.)

People are built in a wide assortment of ways down here. You will want to find an angle that fits most comfortably. Some bottoms are entered most easily with your hand cupped downward. Some will be more easily entered hand cupped up and others will require you to twist and contort till your hand goes in sideways. Many bottoms don't give a hoot, as long as it gets in there. Try not to press hard against any bony structure.

The bottom should be concentrating on pulling you in. Sometimes it helps the bottom to imagine gently expelling you, because if you mildly resist, the bottom is then in a perfect position to pull you in on the next movement. Deep breathing is also a big help. You will have an easier time as your partner exhales.

Often the most sensuous moment of the evening is the gentle slide of your hand into that first cavity. Many bottoms like their first hit of poppers* just before you make that initial slide. Unless your bottom indicates otherwise, enter just as slowly as possible, allowing the bottom to savor every bit.

Once inside, rest a few seconds until the bottom's body has had a chance to adjust. You will usually get an indication by some action of your partner's body (or by your partner grabbing the poppers) that it's time for you to continue.

Often this first slide will require you to pay attention so that your hand ends up in a position comfortable for the bottom; that position may be as a fist or it may be that the passage takes a twist inside and you will need to follow that twist with your hand still in the swan posture. Be sensitive to your partner and you'll know what to do when you get there.

Never forget that you are in a delicate area. You are seeking the direction of the passageway. You do not want to be pressing blindly into the walls.

Your hand is now situated in your partner's rectum. This organ is about eight or nine inches deep. It has the capacity to expand on stimulation. The lower portion swings

---

* The use of poppers is not recommended. For more explanation see Chapter 6.

forward toward the navel because of a strong supportive muscle attached to the pelvic bone. The rectum then swings back and then slightly forward again. These turns make it important for you to feel out where you are going and not push into the walls. It is because of this bend in the rectum that you usually find your best luck in a position where the bottom's legs are at right angles to the body.

Proceeding

The bottom may now ask you to stop in place to rest a second or ask you to come out and go in again, allowing you a chance to regrease. Your partner might just want to feel you slide in another time. Always come out slowly and sensually—never pull out suddenly.

Once you are settled inside, a gentle in-and-out motion (without pulling out of the cavity) will usually help the bottom build confidence in your connectedness. You will rarely stop movement totally after this but maintain some gentle movement.

Allow yourself to be creative, taking cues from the bottom, subtly changing the speed, twist and depth. Remember, lengthy repetition of the same movement at the same spot will likely make the bottom sore. Do not forget to tune in together to the music.

As you work inside, allow your hand to slowly open and your thrust to go slowly (and gently) deeper into the passage. The bottom will likely let you know with groans and moans, whether to proceed or stay right where you are as they wallow in pleasure. You might even try drawing all or most of the way out and slowly sink back in again. As always, the reaction of the bottom will let you know if this is a turn-on.

Blending

As you make love, allow your mind to fantasize what may be going on in the mind of the bottom as the action is taking place. You will probably find yourself also in a dream-like consciousness. Whether or not your fantasies are identical doesn't matter; as you tune into each other, they will mesh and the action will flow.

Be together, enjoying with the bottom what is going on. You can even play with yourself using a free hand, simulating with the hand on your genitalia what it would feel like if that part of you was an appendage as big as your arm, inside of your partner, doing to your partner what that hand is doing. If you can maintain yourself near orgasm for an extended period of time without slipping over, you can build an energy between you and your partner that is without equal.

Rest

Your bottom will probably indicate when it's time for a break. Your bottom may reach orgasm, sense impending soreness, hit exhaustion or just need to rest from the overwhelming intensity. Always listen to the receptive partner's directives on this matter. Remember to come out slowly, perhaps in stages. If possible, maintain the energy of the lovemaking through withdrawal. You will rarely realize how deeply you are in, until you begin to come out.

Sometimes it will be the top who will initiate the break, realizing that the bottom is overdoing it or that the insides are getting dry. Sometimes the top will reach orgasm or just run out of energy. It is amazing how, if the top does reach orgasm, that the bottom can usually sense it and enjoy the sense of drama with you.

If you both reach orgasm, you've experienced one of the great treats of handballing, one that isn't that rare if the top masters holding off orgasm until the bottom catches up. As the old maxim says: "To go together is blessed, but to come together is divine."

Your break may be a few seconds or a major rest period, or perhaps the bottom may have just had enough for the evening. As you become experienced together, the top will be able to gauge how much play the bottom can deal with in an evening. Thoughtful bottoms will make sure that their top's needs are taken care of as well as their own.

Of course, the most pleasure will be had when the two of you are able to change places at the breaks and your partner can return to you the ecstasy you've been giving.

Advanced Technique

Basic handballing is largely intuitive. But when the time comes for you to reach into deeper realms or add a second hand, it especially helps to know what you're doing.

Depth

Beyond the rectum, lies the sigmoid (S-shaped) colon, which takes a double turn, then there are a series of loops opening into successive sections (the descending colon). The number of loops and sections of which you will be conscious depends upon the anatomy and experience of the bottom. If you get some indication that the bottom is ready for deeper exploration, feel around for the first twist of the sigmoid colon and gently work it open with your fingertips.*

Sometimes the twists and loops will give way easily. Sometimes you will have to twist your hand to follow the direction of the passage. Sometimes you will have to reach in with your fingertips and massage deeper into a section before it eases up to accept your full hand. Often you will find success by gently pulling the walls of the inner section down through the loops over your hand until your partner's body just sucks you in right past the loop.

Sometimes the loop will not give way and your partner will register discomfort. This probably means you've reached the limit for that session and you should establish rapport with a different motion lower down in the system.

Depth is just one game to play. A talented butt is like a children's playground. You'll play awhile at the swing, run over to the monkey bars, glide down the slide, then go for the sandbox. If you are tuned in together, your partner and

---

* The rectum and sigmoid colon are very mobile. The descending colon is relatively less mobile, since it is attached to the back wall of the left side of the abdomen. Ninty percent of all tears occur where the sigmoid meets the descending colon, because of the anatomical structure change. Be careful!

the music can tune you into constant creativity.

Of course, the entire process should be gentle and in pace with the flow of the lovemaking. Pay close attention to the reaction of your partner to make sure that what you are doing is agreeable. It's the process that creates the pleasure, not just arriving at some goal.

If you are not discouraged, continue on. All successive loops open in the same fashion, but each will be somewhat different.

In most cases, you should pay more attention to where you are in your partner's system than how much of your arm is inside, unless this seems important to your partner.

Once you have gotten inside a section, many bottoms appreciate it if you establish yourself by gently pulling back and riding in and out to establish yourself comfortably. The character of the energy and the fantasies that accompany this process are established jointly by the two of you.

Even Deeper

If you have continued success, you will eventually reach a loop that will be trickier than the others, taking a strange twist. This is the entrance to the transverse colon (you will likely be about halfway up your forearm by this point). The texture of the inside of this chamber is softer, like fur. Unlike the earlier sections, the transverse colon is not as tightly affixed in place and has more flexibility to move about inside the cavity of the abdomen.

You will likely find depth into the transverse colon a challenge basically because you will have to psyche out the direction it takes, follow it and gently straighten it out, gently pulling it down with your fingers then letting it slide down over your hand.

Deep Trust

If a person allows you deep into their body, they are putting a tremendous amount of TRUST in you. Be extremely gentle and cautious and take all movement slowly. Sudden moves can be very painful. Never do anything that could tear or injure. As more of your arm goes in you may find yourself up against your partner's internal organs. Never press hard against anything. If the bottom wishes you to be up here, the bottom will be encouraging you.

It is apparently a tremendous thrill feeling someone making love to you from deep inside. There is a T-shirt that says: "My heart is yours if you can reach it."

Some highly-experienced bottoms will signal that you exert greater energy or speed, somewhere in the depth process. Always act on the cautious side until you have reached the energy that the bottom seems to be seeking. Always pull out slowly, almost as slowly as you went in, unless the bottom indicates otherwise.

Yes, there are bottoms who crave deep piston action—sometimes right up to the elbow. Always explore gently unless the bottom specifically indicates otherwise and even then carefully work up to what you think is desired, to be absolutely sure that you understand the bottom's meaning.

The Elbow and Beyond

A small number of highly-experienced bottoms open up enough for you to insert your entire elbow and sometimes even the bicep. The elbow, wide and bony as it is, presents a formidable challenge as much for the top as the bottom. You will probably find yourself in a rather awkward position with your arm extended straight out. On a bed, you may find yourself having to lie flat on your back or on your stomach. With a sling, you may find yourself facing away from your partner and your arm reaching behind you.

In order to broaden the anal opening to take your elbow, you will most likely have to twist your elbow at the opening while providing only a minimum of movement with your hand which is, at this point, making its own rate of progress. This twisting will also effectively spread lubricant. Even if the bottom has already taken both of your hands, this stretching may be necessary.

Taking the elbow is rather a treat for the bottom, offering the same kind of "gulp" encountered when the bottom slid over your knuckles to your wrist. Bottoms who learn how to take the elbow easily rarely have trouble grabbing your bicep and even up to the shoulder. Obviously they can go no further and to progress they will have to keep their eyes open for tops with wider and longer arms.

Bottoms who take past the elbows are usually into "performance." A good many are professional singers who have learned to control the insides of their bodies. They are also likely to work out with large dildoes and inflatable toys with the goal of depth in mind.

Punching/Two Hands

While some experienced bottoms crave depth, others crave width, which may eventually translate into inserting both hands (your head, three hands, a Mack truck?). This is not something you do all of a sudden.

Bottoms "into width" will probably indicate particular enjoyment as you pull in and out at the initial entrance of the butt. As you do, you can gradually make your hand wider, until it graduates from a pointed hand into a fist, into a more open fist. It will always need to be just a bit wider coming out than it will be when it goes back in.

When the hand comes all the way out and immediately back in, the process is called "punching." Despite the term, it should not be perceived as something violent. Do it very slowly unless your partner indicates otherwise. Gradually vary the speed, the twist and the motion to keep the bottom from getting sore. The bottom's body will probably give you clues to this process. It is essential that you concentrate when you're punching so that your hand goes back following the same route from which it came out. If you suddenly bend a different way, you could hurt the bottom. This takes practice. Until you master it, err on the side of caution.

If your hand is going in and out easily as a wide fist, it is probably an indication that the bottom would like you to try both hands. At this point you will likely have to take a break to put on a second glove, unless you were prepared in advance for this eventuality.

Three Techniques

To double-up, you do not simply put both hands in together as though in prayer. You must continue the gradual process. There are several techniques that can be used; most likely you will use a combination of the three.

The first technique is to take turns entering with one hand then the other with the fingertips of the second hand going in as the fingertips of the other go out. This will familiarize your partner with both of your hands. Your hands are mirror images of each other and will stretch the bottom in somewhat different ways.

The second technique is to gently enter with one hand while you continually massage the entrance with the fingertips of the other hand. As you go in and out with the lead hand, you lovingly wrap the second hand around the first slowly insinuating yourself until in time both hands go in together or the second hand wraps around the first, already in place. If it is going right, you will find the passage slowly opening to meet you. Never force. This is a slow process and should be approached in a tender, loving way. It should be matched with the satisfied groans of the bottom.

The third technique is often ultimately the most successful. You make a fist with the hand inside the cavity and gently pull it out of the cavity. At the same time, you slowly insinuate the fingertips of the other hand along the inside of the wrist of the hand inside. This creates a feeling of expansion simultaneously on the inside and outside of the sphincter. With the double pressure from both sides, the bottom will often stop being conscious that two hands are pushing in and will just give way to the all-at-once opening of the cavity and the intense pleasure.

Warning

Please do not take these instructions glibly. Few bottoms will ever encourage you far beyond the rectum, and that only with one hand. Unless both top and bottom are highly experienced, the kind of width and depth we are speaking about only happens after many sessions together. If the bottom is new at depth, don't expect to get past more than one loop a night. In fact, it may take many sessions to work past any particular loop. Over a period of time you develop a knowledge of each other and the trust that may make the necessary relaxation possible.

Feet

We had to mention this. Some people see it as the natural progression from the hand. The foot is far less sensitive, but definitely bigger. Make sure that the foot is well pedicured. Lord only knows what latex device you're going to put over it to protect yourselves from spreading micro-organisms.

Never put the entire foot, heel and all, into the bottom. There are many stories (real or fictional) of couples brought to the emergency room interlocked because the bottom tightened up and couldn't let loose of the heel. This story is not funny if it happens to you!

Chapter 5. Technique for Bottoms

A bottom should be familiar with everything the top is going through, but also has need of additional information and techniques.

Learning to Receive

For some people, taking a hand follows a gradual progress from traditional anal intercourse. But for others, it is a process learned over an extended period and with much challenge.

Hypothetically, almost anyone can take a hand inside the rectum. With an anesthetic, a surgeon can easily dilate any-body's anal cavity large enough to insert a hand and perform surgery. Few people have the ability to relax enough to make it easily possible to do at will.

To understand the process of letting go, you need to realize that the anal canal maintains its tubular shape because of two ring-like sphincter muscles about a quarter inch apart, which to some degree overlap.

The external sphincter is controlled by the central nervous system. This is the system which gives us conscious control of the muscles, so that we can, for example, move our arms and legs. Most of us have pretty good control over this first sphincter.

The internal sphincter is controlled by the autonomic nervous system. This system is responsible for most of the functions of our internal organs, like the heart and lungs. We normally have only indirect control of the internal sphincter.

Below the surface of these muscles are the anal cushions, tissues full of blood vessels that fill with blood to become firm, or empty to become flaccid, giving way to entry or exit. Along with the sphincters, these cushions provide the mechanism to regulate excretion from the bowels. Normally, during defecation, the sphincters and cushions relax. If they do not, you have a strained bowel movement. Hemorrhoids are weakness or out-pocketing of the walls of blood vessels in the anal cushions created by such straining.

Most of us are taught from a young age the importance of rigid control over our bowels and flatulance. Through our lives, tensions from all sorts of control and fear issues settle in these muscles, making it difficult for most of us to relax them. This should give new meaning to the term "anal retentive."

The challenge is not learning to stretch the anal canal; rather, it is learning to relax and let go, to allow these muscles to accept entrance from the outside with the same ease they should be allowing release from the inside. Learning to relax these muscles may also help us relax other tensions in our life. It will certainly cut down on the occurrence of hemorrhoids and constipation.

Some people try to loosen up by introducing increasingly larger dildoes and butt-plugs (conical rubber devices). While such devices may be useful for masturbation and stretching, once the anal canal can handle a wrist. The first step is to learn how your sphincters and anal cushions react, so you can take some control over them. This may even help you let go of other stress build-up.

A more effective way to increase control of the internal sphincter and the anal cushions is to spend regular time exploring these parts of your body with your own fingers (clean and lubed, of course). Explore gently. See how this part of your body reacts to deep breathing, to thoughts of fear and thoughts of relaxation. Go slowly and do not push and you will not feel any pain. It isn't necessary to put your entire hand in, which may be awkward.

As you learn what makes your interior react, you can be in better touch with it in a lovemaking situation. Such exploration can even be done in the shower with soap and water.

Pay attention when you have a bowel movement. Learn not to strain and let the body do the work naturally.

Hemorrhoids and constipation are most frequent among people who hold major tension in their anal area. Insufficient ruffage in the diet can contribute to this problem. If this sounds like you, try to eat more fruits, vegetables, nuts and whole grains. The book *Anal Pleasure & Health* [*] by Jack Morin, Ph.D. goes into greater detail on this and many other subjects important to handballing.

Once you have control of the anal cavity, the dildoes and butt plugs will be more useful. They can definitely give you experience in stretching and taking more and more inside of you. Never push these devices, but let your body pull them in. If the body feels attacked, it will react in fear and tighten up. It really is TRUST—the absence of fear—that not only makes taking a hand possible, but makes it the thrill that it can be.

Taking It

Keeping the journey on course is as much the responsibility of the bottom as the top. The bottom needs to remain relaxed. This comes with practice. Breathing deeply, rather than holding your breath helps. Also pulling in, so the top doesn't need to push, can help you avoid what might otherwise be painful. Sometimes pushing out gently as if expelling, then pulling in, can make the difference.

Speak up

The bottom has a responsibility to the top to let the top know if the action is becoming painful or if it even feels like it's going to become painful. The top can always slow down. Pain means that you're going to be sore later or even hurt.

---

[*] Morin, Jack, *Anal Pleasure & Health* (Burlingame, CA: Yes Books, 1981).

There is no reason you should put up with pain. If the top isn't listening, get this person off you and suggest they take out their frustrations somewhere else. This person is not suited as a handball top.

The bottom also has a responsibility to let the top know when it's feeling good. This can be related in words or just in joyous moans. But give all the strokes you can; remember that a top is working hard to make all go well.

If a top is versatile, the top is likely giving it to you just the way the top likes it (or perceives they like it). Pay attention—it's their turn next. However, if the top is a bit off pace, speak up. Everyone is built differently and what may be just right for that person may be wrong for you; your partner deserves your guidance.

Visualize

For some bottoms it helps to visualize what's going on or even watch it in a mirror. For others, it's better to have the mind deep into fantasy. For some, both methods work at different times. The mind will naturally come up with illusions. As you get more experienced you find ones that work and learn to switch to them at the best time. Perhaps you wish to imagine yourself in more traditional intercourse, or to imagine your partner as some desired icon or stereotype. Maybe you'll feel yourself projected into space or perceive the internal movement as the sun creeping over the horizon or a glow of light swelling inside of you. If it works, go with it.

Remember, the idea is to feel wonderful. If your top

has proven trustworthy, allow your body to go with the joy and melt with the ecstasy.

Aprés Play (After the Ball is Over)

After the top has carefully cleaned up the grease from your butt, there are other things you will be thinking about (besides how to stand up).

Blood

The purpose of the intestinal tract is to enable the body to pull nutrients out of your digested food as it passes through. To facilitate this, the inner membrane is very thin with blood-carrying capillaries situated close to the surface.

It is common for this membrane to undergo minor abrasions in the normal course of digestion; this part of your body also heals rapidly. In the healthy body, one's own fecal matter is not going to infect the body through exposure to these exposed capillaries.

What this means is that "a little pink" in the lubricant is no big deal (unless your immune system is severely impaired). It's great when you don't see it, but if you do, don't get bent out of shape. However, if it goes beyond this to drops of blood, it is time to stop playing and wash up. If your immune system is severely impaired, a little pink is time to stop.

Douching

When your system has been worked over, additional douching is irritating to the system and should be avoided. In the remote possibility that there is a minute perforation or tear in the intestine, douching is likely to make it more severe.

Your body can handle the vegetable shortening which is in fact food. Let things work themselves out through gravity.

Soreness

A little soreness inside is common. It usually goes away quickly. It may suggest that the top went in or came out a bit too fast. The most common feeling is that the butt feels like it's "purring."

Sometimes air will work up into the system, especially if there was punching or very active play. This resembles your standard "gas pain" and will work itself out in time. Pressing gently against the pain may help. Sometimes your own finger gently massaging the sphincter or reaching in to massage the first inner loop will make it relax and the air flow out easily.

Another method to deal with gas pain is to lie on your left side, left leg straight, bringing your right knee up as close to the chin as possible

Severe Pain

Yes, it is possible that damage can happen. It usually occurs when the top is unnecessarily rough or the bottom is too drugged up to recognize his or her own limits. When there is a lot of blood that does not stop within a few minutes, or severe pain, do not hesitate to rush to the emergency room of your nearby hospital.

While the entrance of the rectum has many nerve endings, the internal system does not. If there is a tear or perforation, you may not notice it for an hour or two. Internal pain that increases over time is an indication of internal damage. Get it checked as soon as possible.

If you stay away from real sadists and heavy drugs, the chances are probably better that you will get run over by a car crossing the street on the way home than get torn or perforated, but the situation can exist and you should be watchful. Some people never learn to protect themselves. But relax, the hospital can get the situation back in control.

Drowsiness

Feel a bit sickly (drowsy, confused) after a play session? It may be that all you need is fresh air. Open the windows or take a walk. Between heavy breathing, smoke from candles, cigarettes, incense and whatever, compounded by inadequate ventilation, you have likely used up much of the available oxygen in the room. Keeping up the oxygen level in your bloodstream is an important way to protect your immune system. And the air is free!

Food

Following play, you will probably be famished. You may not have eaten most of the day. For this reason it is best to have something waiting that is quick and easy to fix, and substantial to eat. A casserole ready for the microwave is perfect. If you live near town, going out for something might be in order or maybe you can send out for pizza or Chinese food. If you don't have something waiting, you'll probably find yourself hitting the junk food or snarfing up anything your refrigerator contains. Try to plan ahead!

Chapter 6. Substances

The history of esoteric sexual practices always involves a history of mind-altering substances. Handballing is no exception. As the years change, laws and availability change. In the 1970s and 1980s, LSD, marijuana and poppers were the drugs of choice. Other substances, known as MDA, THC, Quaaludes and mescaline went through vogue. LSD is rarely the same hallucinogenic formula it was 20 years ago; MDA, so-called THC (actually a veterinary tranquilizer), Quaaludes and mescaline are rare (although there is word of another substance being called mescaline available in some states). All of these substances are basically illegal in the United States although a number are available legally overseas.

Today there is a different assortment of substances. Some are quite powerful. The term "party favors" is sometimes used to refer to heavier drugs.

The use of any illegal substances and the use of prescription or over-the-counter medication is not recommended (except as advised by a physician or directed on the label). However, it would be naive to think that misuse of such substances does not persist.

This chapter will discuss the most commonly used substances, what they offer those who use them and the risks of misuse or reasons they have been declared illegal.

Poppers

Amyl nitrite, used for angina attacks (cardiac pain) before pill and paste forms became available, was once easily available in fabric-covered ampules. One "popped" an ampule in half to inhale, hence the name poppers. While a prescription was supposedly needed, these ampules were readily available in the 1970s.

In succeeding years, laws cracked down on amyl nitrite but chemists kept coming up with alternative formulas, beyond the laws. These basically had the same effect, but were increasingly more hazardous to the health. These formulas were available in little bottles, marketed under names like RUSH and BOLT. Real amyl nitrite continued to be manufactured and sold illegally.

In February 1991, federal law made the sale of all popper formulas illegal. While a black market continues, quality is undependable.

Let's face the facts. Poppers are dangerous to our health and illegal. If you plan to use them anyway, or plan to travel where they are legal, here's a few tips to cut down the risk.

Free Radicals

A major problem with poppers is a matter of "free radicals." This has nothing to do with politics. It means that the molecules are unstable and attack other molecules in the body, tending to make them unstable. Oxygen molecules in the body respond to the attack, but by leaching oxygen, poppers compromise the body's natural immune system.

However, you can protect yourself to some degree by adding anti-oxidants, high dosage vitamin C, for instance, to your system. One can take 2000 mg. (yes, 2000 to 3000 mg.) of Vitamin C before and after playing. You might also consider 15 mg. of betacarotene daily to further build the system. Both nutrients are inexpensive and readily available.

Effects and Complications

Poppers make you feel suddenly lightheaded, as if you were fainting. With the euphoria, your body relaxes and eases up areas in your body where pressure was building.

Poppers have the desired effect because they are a vascular dilator, which means they open the blood vessels and rush the blood to your head. They also reduce the blood build-up at areas where you have tensed up, such as the anal cushions. The fact that poppers are inhaled, makes them particularly hard on the lungs, and they should never be used if you have lung problems or are running short of breath.

Do not use poppers if your nose is stuffed up. Forced inhalation can send microorganisms and popper fumes into your sinuses and ears, leading to ear and sinus infections. If you feel you must use poppers, at least clear the nasal passages with an antihistamine or nasal spray.

Popper headaches are a sure sign you're doing something wrong. You may be using a particularly noxious formula (abutyl nitrite, the formula they used for RUSH and BOLT is probably the worst). You might try cutting down the amount of poppers you use and make sure they aren't getting stale.

To keep poppers fresh, store them in the freezer. Expose them to air as little as possible. Pouring them from one container to another exposes them to air, as does frequent use. However, if you pour just a small amount into a fresh clean bottle and replace it from time to time, the mother bottle will stay fresh and you should have fresh poppers right down to the end. This also keeps you from using a bottle that is too full. Poppers can be real nasty when you use too full a bottle and spill it in your nose.

Make sure the top of the popper bottle is kept tightly closed. You can even put some plastic tape around the opening below the cap of the bottle before you put it back in the freezer, to avoid minor seepage.

Also be sure not to get grease into the popper bottle; holding greasy fingers over the top will do this. The grease will rapidly degenerate the poppers in the bottle. Try to keep your popper finger greaseless. This is another good reason for using a satellite bottle—if you mess up one bottle you can always wash it out and refill.

If you can get real amyl nitrite, it is the safest for long-term use. However, poppers are illegal and with reason.

Ethyl Chloride

With poppers illegal and difficult to find, handballers have been experimenting with ethyl chloride. But the word is out: Don't!

It made news across the country in 1991 when a Minneapolis man died of a heart attack from inhaling ethyl chloride while having sex. Three deaths in Texas and one in Milwaukee have also been blamed on this substance.

Ethyl chloride, sold commercially as EthlYl Gaz, was developed as an anesthetic, but was dropped from use some 30 years ago because of the high rate of heart failure as a side effect.

The best known death from ethyl chloride occurred in the '60s when a surgeon used the "skin refrigerant" to remove a mole from the back of a fellow surgeon's neck. By draping the head to give himself a sterile field, he created a tent that reduced outside ventilation to the patient.

The patient died because ethyl chloride is a potent inhalation anesthetic and causes people to calmly drift off to sleep without remembering to breath. While asleep under low oxygen situations, ethyl chloride causes cardiac arrythmias. No Breathing = No Oxygen = Death. It's really very simple.

The Minneapolis death was much the same scenario. The man saturated a rag and then covered his face with it until he passed out. In about two more minutes his heart stopped pumping because he wasn't breathing. End of story.

Ethyl chloride is a potent inhalation anesthetic which offers no psychological advantage to a person being handballed except to chemically cut the bottom's brain off the spinal cord. People need to seriously consider their motives if they think they need to remove themselves chemically to have sex. Sex should not be an excuse to wipe out oneself on drugs.

Alcohol

A glass or two of wine or an equivalent amount of beer or hard liquor can be an effective relaxant and get play started in a better mood. However, if the drinking gets much beyond this it cuts into the awareness of what's going on. Handballing requires concentration. Heavy drink makes this concentration impossible. Bottoms on too much alcohol lose touch with their feelings and their pain. Drunk tops are a public menace.

Marijuana

Marijuana (grass, pot) or hashish, a more concentrated form, is usually smoked or cooked into food. It is illegal probably for political reasons, since it is considerably less toxic than both alcohol and tobacco. Like all drugs, it can be habit-forming and provides an excellent way to avoid responsibility and reality, if that is what you're up to. In small quantities, it can be a reasonably safe relaxant which may bring you into other levels of consiousness.

Marijuana lowers your mental defenses. People who have created a complex set of defenses to deal with their everyday problems, often react to marijuana with paranoia.

If this has been your case, it's a good indication that you probably have need of professional help to pull yourself together in a more lasting fashion; you most likely have some deeply repressed problems.

Unlike other recreational drugs, marijuana does not cut down sensitivity or produce an increase in negative side effects with larger doses.

Crystal

Probably the most widely abused drug among handballers is crystal methamphetamines (speed, crank). This is a white powder that can be snorted through the nose, ingested, taken intravenously or shot into the butt with a syringe. While intravenous use is the most dangerous and addictive, all methods can have the same long-term result. Some crystal users maintain themselves for days at artificial levels, shooting up more drugs as they feel themselves coming down; this is called "running" the drug.

Crystal has the unusual effect of making the anal canal and intestinal tract more receptive by deadening unpleasant feelings. It creates a false energy that can lead people to play anally for hours on end. By losing touch with the elements that lead them to feel pain, bottoms are often able to loosen up and take incredibly more than they could otherwise.

The problems are many. For one thing, pain is the body's warning system that something is wrong. Most serious internal injuries in handballing happen to people on crystal because they have lost touch with the pain signals that would have stopped them at points that became dangerous.

This is particularly true when their partner ventures into areas not previously explored. *Crystal doesn't stretch your limits, it makes you lose touch with them!* This is all the more dangerous if the top is not familiar with the bottom and tuned in to the bottom's peculiarities. Situations like this all too frequently result in tears and perforations.

The false energy and passion involved with crystal often makes the players oblivious to details to which they might otherwise be attentive. Crystal players are more likely to forget gloves and share lubricant.

The long-term effects of crystal, however, are the truly scary part. The drug is so pleasant that people playing on it are tempted to use it on a regular basis. Often experience with less addictive drugs leads them to believe that they can use it or not use it at will. Addiction after just a few months of regular use, or just one use of the drug intravenously, is very common. Since most people effectively deny their addiction, they do not realize the problem until they try to stop and discover they can't.

Since speed users quickly learn to associate sex with crystal, they choose to believe that their desire is for sex and the drug is merely an assistance. When they discover how difficult it is to have sex without it, sometimes the truth strikes home. Few people have the moral fiber to give up crystal without going through a recovery program; many discover they must give up handballing (or even all sex) as well, because of the strong association of the two in their mind.

Crystal is highly toxic in the body. It cuts down the appetite, often leading to malnutrition. Crystal addicts are often easily identifiable by creases in their faces running from just to the side of each nostil down to beside the lips. A breakdown in the saliva system in the mouth leads to major tooth decay and eventually the teeth just rot away.

Equally distressing, crystal has a way of breaking down character. Like all addicts, regular crystal users become more concerned with drugs and sex than with friends; they become abusive, mistreat their loved ones, become haphazard about job and other responsibilities. Personnel people know that a pattern of tardiness to work, not showing up or calling in sick on Monday mornings is a sure sign of substance abuse.

Crystal users normally witness a period of severe depression, sometimes lasting several days after use.

Cocaine

Cocaine is a euphoric and anesthetic. It is usually available as a white powder which is snorted through the nose. It can also be shot up intravenously. Coke causes a high not unlike the excitement one feels when one is afraid, but without the unpleasantness. Whatever one is doing seems more enjoyable. Unlike crystal, the effect of cocaine is short-lived, and it must be reused every half hour or so. The sheer cost of cocaine often limits how much can be used. In small doses it might be able to be taken safely. Unfortunately, many people cannot stop with small doses. The news is full of people who turn to crime to support their cocaine habit. It also eats away at the tissue of the nose.

Handballers sometimes shoot cocaine solution directly

into the anal canal with a syringe. Here, beside its euphoric effect, it also acts as an effective anesthetic deadening the feeling in the anal canal to ease entry. Cocaine also tends to cause men to lose their erections, which once again takes pressure off the anal canal.

Cocaine is, like alcohol and crystal, rough on the body, especially the liver. However, perhaps because of the price, it seems to be as much a problem for handballers as it is for the general population, but not more.

Chapter 7. Related Health Conditions

The health conditions related to traditional anal and vaginal intercourse are quite different from those of people who restrict their sexual activity to handballing. Gonorrhea and syphilis and other sexually transmitted diseases spread by exposure to infected semen and vaginal fluids are rarely a problem since handballers began following safe sex practices.

The following advice is very basic; if you have any question you should always refer to a qualified physician.

AIDS*

Around 1981, gay men began coming down with a strange disease that attacked the immune system, making them prey to a myriad of other conditions. The handballing community was hit first and hardest by this condition, lead-

---

* We cannot begin to provide in-depth information about AIDS in this work. Please check medical services, your library or bookstore for a wealth of information on the subject.

ing people to assume that it was handballing that was somehow responsible for the problem. Of those heavy into handballing at that time (mostly men between 25 to 45), perhaps
only five to ten percent are alive today. Most have died
from AIDS (Acquired Immune Deficiency Syndrome).

It was not until about 1984 that enough was known
about the spread of the HIV virus (the apparent main culprit
in the spread of AIDS) for handballers to begin taking precautions such as wearing latex gloves and not sharing lubricant. By that time, however, almost all involved had already
been infected. It is estimated that at least ninety percent of
the men actively involved in handball at this time carry the
virus. Many of those who are still virus-free got into handballing in the last five years.

We now know that the HIV virus is usually spread by
exposure to the blood, semen or feces of an infected party.
Handballing, which was often enjoyed in a group setting,
provided all the necessary elements for disaster.

Handballers often interspersed their play with traditional anal intercourse, rendering the rectum wide-open to
infection. Lubricants were often shared and a hand would go
from one man's butt right into another. Not only that, but
the immune systems of men into handballing had been weakened by other conditions that we will discuss, as well as by
the antibiotics used to treat these ailments. Patterns of heavy
drug use and fast-lane lifestyles didn't help the matter.

By 1988, the evidence was clear that people into protected handballing were far less likely to be exposed to the
AIDS virus than people into protected traditional anal intercourse. The health community has taken a long time to give

its blessings to an activity which is considered so far from the norm and which early on was so closely related to sure death. The problem now is more emotional than scientific.

While most handballers today take the necessary precautions to keep things safe, there remains a hardcore group who refuse to protect themselves and their partners. Often these people are already heavily affected by the AIDS virus and partaking in heavy drugs. For them, drugs and sex provide what they believe to be the quality of their life.

However, medical people have reason to believe that reexposure can lead to the introduction of additional strains of HIV. Some are more deadly than others. We can urge people to play safe; we cannot force them.

For those infected, a healthy lifestyle is the best way to keep yourself from acquiring opportunistic infections related to AIDS. There are a sufficient number of people living with the virus who are maintaining a healthy lifestyle and expressing themselves sexually through handballing to lead one to believe that this can be a positive, healthy way to live.

Hepatitis

Hepatitis Type A offers a greater risk with handballing than other forms of sexual contact. This type of hepatitis (liver infection) is spread through the feces. Even a microscopic amount will spread the infection. No matter how well cleaned out the bottom may be, and no matter how careful the top is not to come into direct contact with butt or lubricant, the chance of spreading this condition will be high.

Fortunately this form of hepatitis is generally not seri-

TRUST / The Hand Book

ous. If you are infected with the condition, you quickly realize something is seriously wrong. The long list of hepatitis symptoms usually includes severe weakness, abdominal pain, dark urine and clay-colored stool.

You are only infectious for about ten days after the onset of symptoms. If you should come down with an infection, see a physician immediately. Be sure to let partners with whom you have had contact know as soon as possible; they can effectively prevent infection with an inoculation of gamma globulin from their doctor or health clinic.

Intestinal Infections

Before AIDS, intestinal infections, especially amoebas, were a major problem among handballers. Many organisms make their home in the digestive tract: some can be pathogenic; some are pathologically neutral; some are decidedly beneficial. These organisms can be transmitted to others through oral contact with feces or can be spread by shared lubricants or anal toys. For this reason, protected safe sex by handballers has made these conditions mostly a problem of the past.

Cramping and diarrhea are reasons to suspect problems with intestinal infections. If these symptoms persist without other explanation, see a physician immediately.

Herpes

Herpes, a common virus affecting the anal area can be spread by fisting if the top is exposed to an area of outbreak.

However, usually a bottom with such an outbreak will avoid the contact as much for self-interest as for care for the partner. Friction makes bumps or blisters all the more painful.

Bottoms can be infectious before an actual outbreak, but this is usually proceeded by itching at the site or flu-like symptoms. Most bottoms have the sense to curtail sexual activity. Recurrent herpes is a common condition among those who have an active HIV condition.

Anal Warts

Anal warts are tiny growths caused by a virus. Clusters form outside the anus and sometimes within the anal canal. They can be spread through sexual or non-sexual means. While they are usually not a problem, they can be painfully irritated by friction. If a partner reports such growth in your anal area or you feel these painful growths, have yourself checked out by a physician. The warts can easily be removed especially if they have not spread too extensively.

Fissures and Fistulas

Fissures are tears or scrapes in the anal area that do not rapidly heal. Fistulas are tiny passageways or "tunnels" that lead from an infected area deeper into the tissue. Fisting rarely causes these problems, but can seriously irritate them. If you have pain in your anal canal that persists, have it checked out by a physician immediately.

Hemorrhoids

Hemorrhoids are rarely a problem of handball bottoms unless they were acquired before handballing was begun. In fact, handballing should effectively prevent their formation. Rectal dilation is even used as a treatment for hemorrhoids in Great Britain.

Hemorrhoids are caused by blood vessels in the anal cushions that swell under undue stress, often bulging out, sometimes in the crease of the butt or even externally. Most people who have learned to take a hand have in the process learned how to relax this area and will take an enema rather than strain in a bowel movement. However, sometimes hemorrhoids will come on with other conditions such as diarrhea and colitus.

If a bottom has an active hemorrhoid, it is wise to relate that to the top. If it is not too severe, the top may be able to avoid unnecessary pressure in that area and not have it seriously affect the play.

Minor Irritations

Often it seems that the anus is the place where all of life's problems collect. There are excellent products available over-the-counter to deal with most minor irritations.

If you have minor soreness the day after playing handball bottom, anesthetic cream for hemorrhoids can make the area feel better. But don't try to mask long-term problems. If pain does not diminish appreciably in a short time, get professional help. (Caution: most hemorrhoidal anesthetics contain benzocaine; about 20 percent of the population are very sensitive to benzocaine and may react negatively.)

If you have an extended period of the runs, protect your anus by keeping it clean and coated with petroleum jelly or antiseptic (antibiotic) ointment. An antibiotic cream or ointment is also good for scratches and shaving nicks. (Another caution: antibiotic ointments usually contain neomycin, another substance to which a fair number of people are unusually sensitive.)

If you have an unexplainable itch on the outside of your anus, over-the-counter cortisone cream or ointment will probably make it feel better. However, if the situation does not improve within a few days, have it checked out; this could be symptomatic of a number of more serious conditions. Some have no relationship to handballing at all.

Chapter 8. Questions and Answers

Are there standards of etiquette, when invited over for handball?

There certainly are. Think about it. It costs a lot of money to entertain: gloves, paper towels, underpads, lubricant, drinks (or whatever it takes to get guests in the mood) and munchies. It normally costs somewhere between $3 and $20 per person to entertain for the evening. No wonder so many people say, "Let's go to your place."

So don't be a freeloader. When invited to play, always bring something: at the very least you can bring a six-pack or a quart of your favorite beverage, your own lubricant and maybe some paper towels. Perhaps you may have the chance to reciprocate, but it's usually the same people who do all the entertaining.

Be neat. If you wash out in someone else's home, be considerate enough to clean up after yourself. Rinse or scour the tub or shower stall, turn the shower nozzle back the way it was, rinse off the tip of the hose in the strongest cleaner you can find and hang the hose back the way you found it.

When you're playing, be conscious where the grease goes and where you stick your greasy hands (please not on the walls). Chances are that someone will have to live in that room after you're finished. Listen for the house rules and respect them.

I have heard of people taking Mydol® before hand-balling. Is it of any value?

Time was when handballers believed that Mydol® would make "taking it" easier and cut down on muscle cramps. Maybe it did, but it's worthless now. They have entirely changed the formula of the "Original" to "New Original" with the same ingredients as Pamprin®. Not only doesn't this help you relax, it includes a diuretic that will keep your bladder filling up—fine for menstruating women, but no help to you. The other Mydol® formulas are equally worthless. Most menstrual medicines are ibuprofen—also no help to us.

Some handballers are experimenting with Momentum® an over-the-counter formula for backache, and Q-vel®, an over-the-counter medication for leg cramps. It may not help anything else, but we get enough leg cramps and sore backs that that won't be totally wasted. There are prescription back medications such as Robaxin® and Soma® that are being used to help bottoms relax. However, be warned of the hazards of using prescription drugs beyond the advice of a physician.

A number of bottoms are using Nupercainal® or Americaine® hemmorhoidal and anesthetic ointments on their butts to extend play and cut down on soreness. They work, but be careful: you may be masking pain that could be a signal that you're getting hurt. Remember too that these ointments usually containe benzocaine, to which many people react badly. Tiger Balm® has long been used for this purpose but it burns before it numbs. Carmex™ for cold sores is gentler. Try a little of this on your butt before you begin. It's harmless and tingles so nicely!

I have heard that vegetable shortening causes polyps in the intestinal tract. Is this true?

Some supposed doctor wrote this in the pages of *Drummer* magazine many years ago. Nothing could be further from the truth. Vegetable shortening is food and naturally flushes through the colon. Another silly column spoke of a nerve that crosses the intestinal tract that could be damaged in handball, but nobody seems to have ever heard of anybody hurt in this way, including physicians.

What is the significance of the red hankie or bandana?

The gay male handkerchief code to help men discover those with complementary interests goes bask to the 1960s when the gay male Levi-leather scene originated. For awhile there were regional variations, but as time passed it became standardized around the world. Red on the right indicates a person who is handball passive and the left means handball active. For many, however, this is only a "first round preference." Because admitting to be bottom is problematic to some men who imagine that it compromises their macho image, there are also a considerable number of men who inappropriately signal left.

Sometimes men will wear their red hankie around their leg or on their arm or perhaps wear something else on one side that is colored red.

The code gets more confused when you add keys which suggest overall dominance. Is a man with a red hankie/right and keys/left advertising that he's versatile or just a very pushy bottom? You'll have to ask him.

Another hankie flag you will see is gray with red in it. This suggests someone who is into bondage or light S&M but also enjoys handball in the scene.

Leather lesbians have adopted and modified the men's hankie code, including red for handball. But it's hard to know whether the red hankie signifies anal or vaginal handball. If you're interested in connecting with her, you'll have to ask!

Since the inception of *TRUST,* some men and women are wearing Trust cloisonné pins and T-shirts. Others wear a red cloisonné pig.

How does vaginal handballing differ from anal handballing?

If the vaginal cavity can afford room for birthing babies, it can also make room for a hand. Some women who have given birth and do not bounce back can take a hand easily, others need to work at it. Women who partake say that it can be extremely exciting and fulfilling. Vegetable shortening is not a good idea in the vagina. Unlike the intestinal tract, the vagina is a closed system and vegetable shortening tends to pool and invites yeast infections. Women into vaginal handballing usually experiment to find the lubricants that work best for them. There seems to be a wide range in tastes.

Women who are experienced in the use of both orifices, and their lovemaking companions, speak of the delight of having a hand in each (of course, this is complicated by the need for two different lubricants). There is just a thin layer of membranes between the two cavities. Wow! Of course, when one hole opens up, it tends to tighten the other, but some women can manage both.

What are the possibilities of handballing two people at the same time?

This creates a real challenge in concentration but it can be a magnificent sharing experience with triple energy present. In order to be successful, the top needs to focus into the energies of both bottoms and coax them into syncronization. This is particularly difficult if the bottoms have a wide variation in experience and internal structure.

It is hard to explain how romantic it can be to be plugged into the energy of a pair of lovers at the same time. It is like being plugged into their relationship. You can feel and touch the affection they have for each other. It is often a big thrill for the couple as well—especially if they can feel the exact sensations that their loved one is feeling at the same time. This is something that it is nearly impossible to do without a skilled third party.

Is simultaneous handballing possible?

Possible? Yes. But difficult and rarely very satisfying because it is difficult to concentrate on your own needs and that of the other person at the same time. Also the logistics are such that no matter what position you use, you will not have much latitude for creativity. The same goes for daisy chains where a number of people are simultaneously plugged into each other. It works, but it rarely works well, though the idea certainly does inspire the imagination.

Is it unusual to have a desire to urinate when taking a hand?

This is very common since the hand will likely put pressure on the bladder from the inside. If it is at all full, you'll want a chance to get up and empty it. Since an enema will often lead to water in the bladder, it is good to do this a few hours before you begin.

There are some bottoms who find pleasure urinating

through the entire process. Hopefully, the top will be prepared with a towel and just go with the joy of the bottom.

Should the bottom touch the genitalia, while being handballed?

Touching the genitalia will normally tighten the sphincter. If the top is not already inside this will make it that much more difficult to enter. However, if the bottom is having trouble taking it, touching the genitalia may just offer the relief of orgasm.

Once the top is inside the first sphincter, the choice of touching the genitalia is a very personal one. Some bottoms like to remain aroused in this fashion, some do not.

Does a bottom reach orgasm when getting handballed?

If the bottom wishes to do so. Many bottoms experience internal orgasms as significant as external ones. Some never reach an external orgasm and couldn't care less. Some sometimes do. Some always do. Some reach orgasm as soon as you slip inside.

There are also some bottoms who will want you to keep going after they reach orgasm or slip out and go right back in. Pay attention!

Do people really stuff each other with fruit, vegetables and other foods?

Yes, they do. People are always searching for variety. Peeled bananas are perfect for this, so are hard boiled eggs. They aren't going to do the bottom any damage and they feel good. Make sure the eggs are shelled and have had a chance to cool. It's always amazing to see how many of these will slip in. If you use other produce (i.e. eggplants, grapes, sausage, bologna, cucumbers) make sure they are perfectly smooth and that any possible pesticides have been washed off. Remember, what goes in will come out. Never put anything into your rectum that has edges, points, wires or that could open up or get stuck. Reaching in to grab and pull this stuff out may or may not be pleasant. Of course, always wash out before experimenting and make sure that items are well lubricated before entry.

Is handballing S&M (sado-masochism)?

Many of us prefer to think not. But all sex, even the most conventional, has an edge of pain to it. To reach higher levels of pleasure you may find yourself enduring what might otherwise be thought of as discomfort or pain. But the pain can heighten the effect of the pleasure. It's like the commercial bakeries that load cookies with salt, so they can put more sugar in them.

There are people who enjoy an S&M fantasy in their sex, who combine this with handballing. Things are fine as long as it's fantasy and both partners know that the interior

93

of the digestive tract is no place to be inflicting real pain. Unfortunately, some tops on power trips forget this and can damage bottoms who have not learned to endure this sort of physical torment. Some bottoms seem to thrive on it!

If you're a bottom and you choose to deal with someone of this sort (and they almost always give you signals in advance), you do so at your own risk.

Does handballing encourage hemorrhoids?

Quite to the contrary, most people who have learned to take a hand learn to relax this area and are less prone to hemorrhoids. Handball bottoms are more at ease with enemas and are less likely than others to put up with constipation, a major cause of this condition.

Can frequent handballing lead to incontinence?

Once again, to the contrary. Handballing trains the bottom how to control the sphincter muscle. The bottom learns how to relax and how to tighten and is less likely to lose control than others without this exercise.

How is the prostate effected in handball?

For men, the prostate gland, located about two to three inches into the anus, is a major source of pleasure in rectal penetration. This organ responds beautifully to massage and encourages orgasm. For this reason, it may need to be avoided in some men, so that orgasm does not happen too quickly. You will have to learn from the bottom whether this is the case. Some men will draw you in deeply and discourage you from coming too far out, knowing that massage on the prostate will lead to orgasm and the end of the session.

Most men love to have their prostate played with, at sometime or another. It grows harder as the bottom approaches orgasm and deflates on arrival. It should always be rubbed and never poked. Often if a man on the bottom cannot handle your entire hand, he may still be able to enjoy your fingertips massaging this gland. Rub deeply between the ridges and watch him go wild.

It is believed that men whose prostate glands are gently massaged are less likely to have prostate problems in their later years.

Does the size of one's hand make a difference?

Yes, it does. A small hand can usually navigate more easily. A slender hand that can compress down to nothing is a benefit. But the size will never be as important as the sensitivity the top has to the needs and subtle internal instructions of the bottom. Some experienced bottoms prefer large hands.

Does it make a difference if one uses the left or right hand?

It does to some people, who swear they have a left-handed or right-handed butt. Of course, you will have to switch hands if you turn the bottom upside down. Most people just use their stronger hand unless requested otherwise.

What kind of reactions do people normally have after being handballed?

They are usually too overwhelmed to move for a couple of minutes. Sometimes they will quiver or even tremble for a minute or two. These signs usually mean all goes well. Often they will express gratefulness to the top. They may register an immediate need to go to the bathroom. Afterwards, the butt is often said to feel like it is "purring."

There is sometimes some soreness. This may suggest that the bottom put up with more pain than would have been well advised.

Any hints for dealing with a novice or person who is still unsure as a bottom?

(1) Make it clear that the first and only priority is for them to feel good. There should be no reason for performance anxiety. If things don't reach any particular point but the bottom has a wonderful experience, that is just fine. It is better to make less headway than to push and scare the bottom from trying again. Sometimes it takes several or many attempts. So be it. *A bottom should never put up with any pain.* You can always go more slowly.

(2) Impress the bottom with the fact that it is their responsibility to pull, not yours to push. You will only give them what they desire. Maintain a gentle pressure, but never

force anything.

(3) Make it clear that "stop" means stop in place and "out" means that you will slowly withdraw. Expect them to test you.

(4) Be caring, sensitive and always keep your word.

Should a person with AIDS or ARC (AIDS Related Condition) be handball receptive?

The technically correct answer to this question is that you should follow the advice of your doctor. Unfortunately, many physicians know little or nothing about anal sex or handballing and react to all such questions with an emphatic negative. Others feel that doing without sex is the rightful retribution for the "sins" that gave you this condition. Don't buy this garbage. If a doctor can't give you a logical explanation and you can't change doctors, you will have to use your own judgment.

The healing of love and the pleasure and relief of sex go a long way to make the quality of life bearable, especially when you have a life-threatening condition. Is there any problem with your lower digestive tract? Will washing out cause any unnecessary problems? Do you have an active herpes infection or any condition that could be contagious or uncomfortable to you or your partner? Does your partner know your situation? Can you enjoy handballing without toxic substances or trauma that will upset your system? In the final analysis the decision will be yours alone.

"Seek, therefore, a large trailing gourd, having a stalk the length of a man; take out its inwards and fill it with water from the river which the sun has warmed. Hang it upon the branch of a tree, and kneel upon the ground before the angel of water, and suffer the end of the stalk of the trailing gourd to enter your hinder parts, that the water may flow through all your bowels. Afterwards rest kneeling on the ground before the angel of water and pray to the living God that he will forgive you all your past sins, and pray the angel of water that he will free your body from every uncleanness and disease.

"And if there remains within you aught of your past sins and uncleanness, seek the angel of sunlight. Put off your shoes and your clothing and suffer the angel of sunlight to embrace all your body. Then breathe long and deeply, that the angel of sunlight may be brought within you . . . For I tell you truly, holy is the angel of sunlight who cleans out all uncleanness and makes all evil-smelling things of a sweet odour. None may come before the face of God, whom the angel of sunlight lets not pass."

—The Essene Gospel of Peace
Translated from the Aramaic in 1933
Attributed to Jesus Christ

PART TWO

THE SPIRITUALITY OF HANDBALL

The Chakras

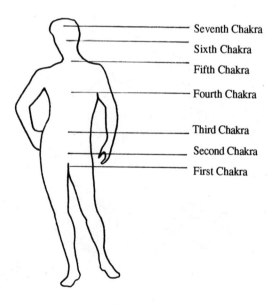

Seventh Chakra
Sixth Chakra
Fifth Chakra
Fourth Chakra
Third Chakra
Second Chakra
First Chakra

Chapter 9. The Kundalini

To understand the spiritual aspects of handball, one needs to step back and take a totally different approach to spirituality than is understood in traditional Christian thought. Such an approach runs parallel and in no way contradicts traditional concepts. In fact, in many ways it offers evidence to great spiritual truths we can otherwise accept only on faith.

The concepts that I will draw in this chapter may seem as off the wall to many readers as the sexual frankness of the first portion of this book. But readers who find the first part of the book an everyday experience will be able to read this part and get a notion of how strange the uninitiated must find their reality!

Basic Concepts

To understand the spirituality of handballing, we must understand the concept of the Kundalini. This is based on an understanding of body energies that is more basic to Eastern thought. We must look at the material body as being the home of an energy body that takes roughly the same space as the matter body. The Indians call this energy *prana*. The Chinese call it *chi*. Western terminology refers to it as etheric or vital energy. While it eventually takes the overall shape of the body (perhaps protruding beyond the body by a fraction of an inch), it has its own system of flow, which is quite complicated, but eventually fills the contours of the entire body.

The major flow of vital energy runs through several meridians running up and down the body, parallel to the spinal column. The entire system is laid out in detail by Chinese medicine, whose practitioners use it as the guidelines for acupuncture and acupressure. It is the seemingly uncanny success of acupunture that is forcing Western science and medicine to take this system seriously. But Western science is very slow to give up its holy cows.

Vital energy is not all of like kind. Within us we carry energy of varying frequencies. Developing energies of higher frequency is a part of growing spiritually, as we will better understand as this chapter develops.

At key junctures on the spinal meridians are power centers, seven major ones. These are often referred to by the ancient Sanskrit name of *chakras* (Sanskrit is an ancient language of India). There are also a number of minor chakras on the body (i.e. elbows, shoulders, knees).

The major chakras are home base for the frequencies of energy that make up human character. How these energies get translated to the brain to create the thoughts of which we are conscious is difficult to comprehend, but apparently this is part of the system.

One of the gifts of people we call clairvoyants is the ability to visualize the vital energies. Most clairvoyants have learned to keep their gifts to themselves in order not to seem strange or crazy to others. Many block this gift. Clairvoyants often become substance abusers, because drugs and alcohol effectively block this sight. Clairvoyance in our culture is more a curse than a gift.

Somewhere between one and ten percent of the population are to some degree clairvoyant. Few will own up to it; they've learn to protect themselves by keeping it to themselves. Actually it is no more magical than the fact that a portion of the population is colorblind. But, while others will easily accept people who see *less* than they see, they are downright hostile to people who see *more*!

Many, but not all, clairvoyants see the energy that emanate from the chakras as a rainbow of colors. By identifying the color, one can identify the energy in action. This is the basis for what is called auras and it also provides the groundwork for what is commonly called "mindreading." Dismissing this as simple is a great injustice; the visual forms that this energy takes is quite complicated and the sophistication of those who have learned to analyze it is dazzling.

However, to understand the chakras one doesn't need to be a clairvoyant or "mindreader." A basic knowledge of the world they see is sufficient.

The Seven Chakras

The seven chakras are best introduced from the bottom up. They run analogous to levels of character (and hence spiritual) development of individuals. It may be understood that the most spiritually immature people are functioning at the lowest chakras. As individuals grow in maturity, their primary energy emanates from progressively higher chakras. The basic color of their aura changes with the highest chakra developed.

The Root Chakra

The first or root chakra is located at the base of the genitalia, where they meet the bottom of the anus. The energy generated here is the basic energy of animal survival. It harbors the basic will to live and protect one's life at all costs. The manifestations of people acting wholly from this chakra are hostility, violence and competitiveness. Here other people are perceived as mere vehicles to satisfy one's own basic lusts.

The color of the first chakra is red. This is the kind of red that one senses in mob scenes, when the energy is so intense that even the normally non-clairvoyant see in their mind's eye a glimpse of this intense energy. Regrettably, a majority of the earth's population runs primarily from the first chakra. For these people, life is truly a dog-eat-dog existence.

The Second Chakra

The second chakra, located near the genitalia, is associated with sexuality. The color is orange. The color is prominent in people engaging in sex, sexual thoughts and in pubescent adolescents. Often the color is merely a visual transition between red and yellow.

The Third Chakra

The third chakra is located in the solar plexus, the central abdomen. This is the energy center of the body. The color is yellow. This chakra relates to power and control. This chakra relates to the ego, the "look how important I am" tendencies in us. People functioning primarily at this chakra are likely bent on controlling others. They are often pushy and uncaring.

Most sexuality is limited to the first three chakras, the "lower chakras." Sex in the lower chakras is about animal desiring, "getting off" and power games. Affection and caring have little place here, though for some they may be given lip service.

The Fourth Chakra

Those who are following the logic of all this will probably have already guessed that the fourth chakra is located around the heart and relates to love, affection and caring. This chakra relates to two colors. Green is the basic color; it suggests love of self, self-esteem—the necessary basis of all love.

When love extends to others, the energy of the fourth chakra becomes pink, the color of compassion. Pink energy is also healing energy. If this information seems to lead into all sorts of clichés, it is no coincidence.

People functioning from the fouth chakra are people who live from their compassion, people driven by their concern for others. Often these people become heath providers, social workers or devoted parents.

Fourth chakra love is unconditional love. What people working from lower chakras call "love" is a deal—"you give me what I want and I'll give you what you want." The mother of high character who faithfully visits her child in prison, no matter what her child has done, is a prime example of unconditional love.

When you enfold a child or a loved one in your arms in a nurturing embrace, you are most likely enfolding them in a pink energy, which they interpret as warm and loving.

The Fifth Chakra

The fifth chakra is located at the throat and mouth. The color is blue. This is the creative chakra; it relates to communication and understanding, the interrelatedness of all things. People functioning at the fifth chakra feel they have work to do and things to accomplish.

Gifted artists, writers, teachers are often people functioning from the fourth chakra as well as people with a mission who start organizations or fight for justice.

The Sixth Chakra

The sixth chakra relates to the "third eye" of metaphysics. This is the energy of intuitive wisdom. It suggests a knowingness of what is to be done. While all of us have a piece of this in what we know as our conscience, a person functioning at the sixth chakra has a clear knowledge as to what he or she must do with his/her life. The color of the sixth chakra is indigo or cobalt blue. This is the color of mysticism, of direct connection with the universal.

The Seventh Chakra

The seventh chakra represents a being beyond knowingness. It is the spiritual chakra. Its energy is violet. It is seen in people who live a meditative life, people deeply involved in spiritual work. It is very rare. Usually individuals working primarily from the fifth through seventh chakras show aspects of all these energies at different times.

Occasionally clairvoyants see a clear crystal aura coming from people who have graduated beyond the primary aura system into higher levels of spiritual consciousness, or they may see intense rainbows or even colors beyond the ordinary spectrum.

A person who is spiritually evolved and well-balanced works from all seven chakras. Those who let the lower chakras become blocked while functioning at the higher chakra are thought of as "airy" and lacking in "grounding."

Exploring Levels of Consciousness

To a person dealing from a particular chakra, at a particular level of consciousness, the energies of that level seem as ordinary as one working at any other level. It is only when a person jumps to a higher level or descends to a lower level that she or he notices something out of the ordinary.

The power of the acid taken in the hippy days was its ability to momentarily throw people into levels of consciousness higher than those to which they were ordinarily familiar. Impressions of love and oneness with the universe were really only momentary glimpses of life at the higher chakras. When the spiritual seeker Baba Ram Dass gave a strong hit of acid to a spiritual master, the master reported no reaction at all—he'd already seen it all.

We also speak of peak experiences. These are times in our lives when we felt in touch with greater forces than in our ordinary condition. Sometimes these are times of great accomplishment or visits to spiritual places, the tops of great mountains or places with vistas that stretch beyond the imagination. These are likely times when we reach up to touch levels of consciousness beyond those with which we normally deal.

Religion vs. Spirituality

Most of what common people know as religion is rules set up by authorities (religious or secular) to supposedly protect people from their own "lower nature." Within the inner circles of true religions are the mechanisms for indi-

viduals to grow spiritually and develop the "higher nature."
This is the purpose of the monasteries of all religions.

What Eastern cultures call "yoga" or union are physical
paths to bring the individual in touch with his or her higher
aspects. Kneeling in church may be seen as yoga, just as
much as the medititive positions of the Buddhists.

Tantric Yoga

Tantric Yoga refers to a school of yoga, which has been
traced back to ancient India but may even go back way
before that. Its methods are comprised of physical and
mental disciplines designed to help the participant focus the
mind and take control of the forces that develop the higher
chakras.

A primary concept of Tantric Yoga is the Kundalini.
This is best understood as a metaphor of a snake or serpent
which is at normal times wound tightly at the base of the first
chakra.

As an individual develops spiritually, the serpent
uncoils and travels up the path of the chakras, setting into
action one after the other in its travels. When the Kundalini
stretches up, beyond and through the crown chakra, the
individual knows the meaning of ecstasy as all chakras are
aglow and the individual realizes the bliss possible when the
human makes connection with the divine.

For those on a spiritual path, development through the
chakras is seen as the most important work of a lifetime, or
perhaps many lifetimes. It is a path of growth beyond individual ego to responsibility and connectedness to all things.

Spiritual vs. Secular Life

It is one of the mistakes of people bound by mundane reality to think that the spiritual and the secular life are two unrelated things. This could not be further from the truth. The difference between the spiritual and the secular is what an individual makes spiritual or secular. One person's "holy space" may be mundane or even a degraded area to someone else.

Working, eating, sexuality, even defecating can be spiritual to one who keeps the spiritual in mind. In Buddhist monasteries there are special shrines in the bathrooms to remind followers to keep even this activity holy. The Hari Krishnas carry prayer beads close at hand, much like those of the Catholic clergy, to remind them of the spiritual presence. While religionists like to believe that they are conjuring up God or some divine entity, what they are really doing is bringing forth the divine in themselves and attempting to bring a spiritual truth to whatever is going on around them.

Sex can be sacred or profane, depending on how you approach it. A person striving to make life more spiritual will make sex spiritual, as well.

Handball as Tantric Yoga

As we have mentioned several times earlier, handball is one of the most intense interactions that two human beings can witness. A top plugged in to the rectum and descending colon of the bottom is also physically plugged into the energies of the bottom's lower three chakras.

Of all parts of the body, the hand is most effective for focusing and projecting vital energy out of the body. It is the hands which are principally used by healers as well as magicians. This is the part of our body with the greatest ability to connect outwardly and with the greatest flexibility to respond to the directives of our mind.

When the top is truly plugged into the energy of the bottom at a Tantric level, there is a synergy. Both partners are propelled into a different level of consciousness. How much of a change occurs would depend on the spiritual level of each partner, the amount of energy of each individual and what each partner is giving to the interaction.

It has been said that in "normal" sex there are four present—two minds and two bodies. When there is real closeness, perhaps there are two present—two body-minds in embrace. In Tantric sex there is only one present—two minds and two bodies locked into one, there is no top and there is no bottom. When you reach a Tantric lock it is as if you are both suspended in space, the energy of the interaction takes over and the individuals break down into one entity of energy cruising through the universe as it will go. It has been spoken of as a touching and inter-locking of souls.

The partners progressively lock together at each chakra, The energy grows until the energies of both parties shoot out the crown chakra into the eternal. One may witness more Kundalini energy than some yogis may find in a lifetime.

A great deal of what happens between the partners can be enhanced by the kind of energy that the top is projecting. This includes the thoughts and emotions of the top as well as what kind of energy the top has available. When the top is projecting loving, nurturing fourth chakra (pink) energy it is immediately felt by the bottom who resonates at the fourth chakra. Spiritual thoughts can bring the higher chakras into play. These might involve ideas of seeing yourself and/or your partner as an angel or heavenly vision or maybe even lovingly imagining your partner as Christ being impaled on the cross. Perhaps you will even feel purple flames extruding from your hands.

Is this Tantric lock present in every handball episode? Most decidedly not. While it may happen helter-skelter between any two partners whether they are seeking it or not, it most often happens between spiritually advanced people who do not have to overcome barriers.

The barriers are many. In fact, for a good many people involved with handball the Kundalini effect backfires. In order to carry forth, the Kundalini energy must be able to reach from chakra to chakra. If one of the individuals is badly blocked at a particular chakra and the other partner is not strong enough to overcome the barrier or is also blocked, the energy bounces back and creates an overload at the lower chakras.

An overload at the first and second chakras presents itself as an insatiable compulsion to have more and more sex or to constantly masturbate—there is an internal need to release the excess energy. An overload at the third chakra leads to an excessive power trip. Tops stuck at this level can be dangerous as they are doing something *to* you instead of *with* you. Bottoms stuck at third chakra are real pushy, putting their tops through their paces. Pushy bottoms become a real bore very quickly.

Handballing confined to the lower three chakras is an intense sensual experience with strong animal overtones. Partners often speak of themselves as "pigs" and get off on the demeaning nature of the experience. This is the province of sleaze, of power trips, of dehumanizing self and each other. Affection has little place in such interaction, and partners often turn their back on each other after the experience, as strangers passing in the night.

Certain drugs create a barrier at the second or third chakra and sustain the animal, sexually-obsessive behavior. Methamphetamines (speed, crystal) is beyond a doubt the worst offender. Handballers on speed can often carry on for as much as half a day to two days, with both parties having little memory of what transacted. Afterwards they may treat each other impersonally. Heavy doses of alcohol and cocaine can have a similar effect.

Speed users often find that everything on their mind seems somehow colored by the need for sex (being stuck at the lowest chakras). Sex and speed become a single entity. Addiction is only a matter of time. A breakdown in character and integrity is the eventual result unless the individual is able to somehow break the sequence.

Androgyny

As Purusha* (Peter Allison Larkin) discovered over a decade ago, the concept of androgyny is a key element in

---

* Larkin, op. cit.

understanding what he called "cosmic erotic ecstasy"—the
ecstatic nature of handballing. Completion as a human being
requires getting over the artificial cultural bridge that has
for so long divided the sexes. The violent, competitive
macho man and the passive, clinging, dependent woman are
half-people unable to provide the character elements necessary for spiritual completion.

Spiritual traditions have been pretty much in agreement
that one must come into balance, become both aggressive and
nurturing, to reach the spiritual heights. Jesus and St.
Francis were such people, so was the Buddha and the Taoist
Immortals. One must find the peace of one's being and
project it onto the outer world. In the Gospel of Thomas,
one of the Gnostic Gospels (the Nag Hammadi) unearthed
around 1945, Jesus tells the people when they can expect to
enter the Kingdom of Heaven:

"When you make the two One,
and you make the inner as the outer,
and the outer as the inner,
and the above as the below,
so that you will make the male
*   and the female into a single One,*
in order that the male is not made male
nor the female made female.
When you make eyes in place of an eye,
and a hand in place of a hand . . .
Then shall you enter the Kingdom.

Handballing provides the possibilities of sexual androgyny. Purusha projected that homosexuals, freed of conventional stereotypes, may be at an advantage to reaching such a balance. I would suggest that it is a challenge each of us must face for ourselves.

Chapter 10. Questions and Answers

Are there other spiritual possibilities in handballing?

There certainly are. Partners sometimes believe they have been transported to past (or simultaneous) lives together. One person reports experiences with a partner that took him to Renaissance Italy. With a partner of Mexican descent he has felt witness to rituals of Mayan or Aztec Indians. Other people have reported throwbacks to Ancient Tibet.

Some handballers feel the presence of saints and spiritual masters joining in their lovemaking. Sometimes they take over one or the other, or they just may be with both. Clairvoyants report "seeing" at such times the presence of outside "entities." Sometimes there are animals present, which may relate to the power animals dealt with in Shamanism, the spiritual practice of many native peoples including the Hawaiians and Native Americans.

People playing under the influence of heavy alcohol, hard drugs or some negative or satanistic space may find themselves conjuring up demons and negative forces. This may make the play very hot, though goodness knows what the long-term effect might be!

Is the Kundalini effect something that happens to only one partner?

If it is to happen at all, it will happen to both together. Energy is not a static thing: it flows. Often a top building up this energy will put his head to the body of the bottom or touch the breast or lips of the bottom to create an energy cycle which both partners will feel. Strangely enough, according to Tantric teachings the top often is more effected by the Tantric experience than the bottom.

It is particularly exciting when the top is working from the fourth (pink, loving) chakra. As romantics have said for thousands of years the power of love has no limits. The love energy is like an endless fountain and can give the top the ability to keep up the high level of energy for extended periods of time.

What are the short and long term results of the Kundalini effect?

When the Kundalini is fully excited the feeling is overwhelming. It is often compared to giving birth or traveling into a different universe It is for some the most ecstatic

117

moment they have ever witnessed.

From the moments that it happens there is a cleansing and healing. Sick people often come out of the experience feeling to some degree revitalized. This is particularly true for people with AIDS and other systemic conditions.

Whether your long-term spiritual growth is stimulated by these short-term experiences depends on how you respond to this experience through the rest of your life. These moments of ecstasy can be perceived as a sample of the kind of blissful states one reaches as one progresses spiritually. For some, it has set them out on a trail to capture this ecstasy for more of their life.

However, more sex is not the answer. The sex provides a short-cut, a short-circuiting of the system so to speak. It cannot last more than a few minutes. It can provide, however, a continuing reminder of one's spiritual possibilities and can be perceived as a glorious affirmation of the wonders of the spiritual path.

Sex as an end to itself is meaningless. But it can be a means and a point of departure.

Does the spiritual development of your partner make a difference?

You will have a much easier time reaching a spiritual lock with someone who is more rather than less spiritually developed. Sometimes people can really surprise you. Someone who seems dull or uninteresting in their external demeanor can have thrilling energy inside and the reverse, as well. People who are very negative will be more difficult to tune in with. Be careful, often people's negative energy can blend into yours and you will find yourself angry or unhappy without explanation.

Some bottoms are energy vampires. They literally suck you dry offering nothing in exchange. After you are with such people you feel drained and used. They are probably not people you will wish to be with again.

What do clairvoyants see when experiencing or watching others in the Kundalini experience?

They speak of a dazzling array of colors, almost neon in intensity compared to their normal visions. There are tremendous amounts of cobalt blue in the room. The two partners may begin to glow a neon raspberry (a combination of pink and violet). Clear crystal light emanates from the top of their heads. There will likely be the outlines of additional protective entities present in the room.

Can you add ritual to your session?

If you're both into it, this can be great. It can put you on the same wavelength and change the tenor of your interaction from the casual or profane into the sacred.

Most people react positively to a smudge stick (a bundle of special greens that smolder to make a cleansing fragrance—from the Native American tradition). This seems to discourage negative energies. One just waves the stick between you in a deliberate fashion, forming whatever pattern seems to work. Feel free to create your own ritual.

If playing in a group, you can form a ring and encourage each person to play with the nipples of the person on either side. This lays the groundwork for a loving group energy.

Groups can really add to the energy of handballing. Take turns with each partner being the bottom with the rest of the group assisting and tuning in to the pleasure of the bottom. After everyone has had their turn for full attention, then people break down in whatever configuration they wish. The important factor being that nobody feels left out and that the group affection is maintained.

Is it possible to reach the Tantric energy without actually being inside your partner?

Yes, it is. Sometimes one will have to come out of the bottom for some reason, but if a high level of energy transfer has been reached the energy can continue with the top just pressing the fingertips gently against the outside opening.

Is the Kundalini something unique to Tantric Yoga?

No, an analagous sytem is found in the secret teachings of spiritual groups everywhere in the world. The African Zulus call it "the fire of the gods." In the Mayan teachings it is called *hurakan* or "lightning" and the chakra center are depicted with animal symbols.

Index

The Author

photo by Emlyn Wynne

Bert Herrman is editor/publisher of *TRUST / The Handballing Newsletter* and author of *Being • Being Happy • Being Gay*, the leading book on building gay/lesbian self-esteem. He is publisher of Alamo Square Press, offering books and periodicals to serve the gay/lesbian community. Herrman is a graduate of the Wharton School, University of Pennsylvania and holds a master's degree from the Ohio University Graduate College. He resides in the Castro District of San Francisco.